CW00542168

HORSE DRAWN

FARM IMPLEMENTS

Tribute to the Plough Team

Yet are they there in Autumn's gold and mellow day,
Ever listening for that voice which bids their thoughtful stride;
Still do they lean and strain to pierce the umber'd clay;
Long may we work them, and their willingness abide.
Blow, wind, across the furrows; shine, sun, upon the Earth;
Before us lies this heritage of honesty, and worth.

Claudia Steele

Painting by Joe Godderidge

HORSE DRAWN
FARM IMPLEMENTS

EDWARD HART

Contents

First Published 2003

Copyright © Edward Hart 2003
The moral rights of the author
have been asserted

All rights reserved. No parts of
this publication may be repro-
duced, stored in a retrieval system, or transmitted, in any form
or by any means, electronic,
mechanical, photocopying,
recording or otherwise, without
prior permission of Japonica
Press.

ISBN 1-904686-03-6

A catalogue record for this book
is available from the British
Library

Published by
Japonica Press
Low Green Farm, Hutton,
Driffield,
East Yorkshire, YO25 9PX
United Kingdom

Book layout by Banks Design

Dedication

This book is dedicated to JOHN HARRIS of EPWORTH, North
Lincolnshire, whose unstinted generosity with knowledge and photo-
graphs made a major contribution to this book.
Sadly, John died in 2002, before the publication of "Horse Drawn
Farm Implements"

About the Author

Edward Hart has written twenty-five books on horses, farming and the countryside. He developed his love of horses when helping on farms as a schoolboy in the Vale of York. He then became a farm worker for seven years, followed by farming on his own in Bilsdale, North Yorkshire, before turning to agricultural journalism.

In this book Edward Hart traces the development of ploughs and cultivators, carts and waggons, drills, mowers and other implements over the past century and beyond. He considers himself very lucky to have caught the last days of the big farm staffs, whose teaching methods were uncompromising and direct. He learnt to plough with horses, and used many of the implements described here.

As a student at Askham Bryan College, Edward won the Yorkshire Agricultural Society's Gold Medal, became a Nuffield Scholar, and later won the Hydro–Agri/Guild of Agricultural Journalists Award for best feature on the environment, followed by a Farmer's Fund Scholarship to study hefting of hill sheep. He is Heavy Horse Correspondent for Horse and Hound and a regular contributor to Heavy Horse World, The Ark, The Daily Telegraph, The Yorkshire Post, Country Illustrated, and a range of other magazines. He gave the Annual Bakewell Lecture to the Dishley Society on the History of the Heavy Horse.

He also collects and sells books on livestock and country subjects. A keen cricketer and a devotee of field sports, Edward Hart is known to a wide circle of country people. Among his early friends were the men whose lives revolved around the farm horse, and this book is a tribute to them.

Foreword

by Clarissa Dickson Wright

Today's children see horses at a distance. For a town child, there is the excitement of a brewery dray in the street, or a platoon of horse soldiers exercising. A country child has the joys of Pony Club and the Hunt. There is racing on the "telly", and sometimes showjumping or eventing, but it is hard for any of us to remember how recently the horse was not only pleasure but the necessity of our lives.

I recall being told with amazement that the German Army's transport in World War Two was almost entirely horse-drawn. My grandmother had friends whose coachmen became their chauffeurs; indeed my grandmother had the first car in Singapore, and her sister had a panic attack when travelling at 15mph until tersely told how fast a horse galloped. The photographs of London with its horsedrawn vehicles are actually quite late in the 20th century, and I love to dwell on the fact that it takes longer to get to Grange-over-Sands by public transport than it took by stage coach.

This delightful book brings to us so many memories of an age not long gone. For me it is an interesting trip into nostalgia, as well as a splendid source of information. For the historian, it is a serious work, and for those of us who love and respect horses it is a fascinating study of the harness and furniture that enabled them to play such a role in our daily lives.

I am sure you will enjoy this book as I have, and go away from it much better informed as to the ingenuity that allowed man's strongest ally to serve us.

Introduction

A fine pair drilling corn.

Why a book on horse-drawn farm implements? One reason is to interest the growing number of people who wish to work their horses rather than merely show them. At scores of those spectacular summer agricultural shows that grace our summer season, classes are being staged for implements as well as for carts and waggons.

Spectators fall into two classes. 'I remember my grandfather working one of those', say some, while the opposite rejoinder is: 'I've never before seen anything like that!'

The huge range of farm implements is testimony to the ingenuity of men using the limited technology available to them. Wood from the local timber yard and iron and steel from the nearest foundry encompassed most of their basic materials. From these were evolved harrow and plough, cultivator and scruffler, drill and mowing machine. Then came the self-binder and various ingenious devices to use horse power to lift hay, chop turnips and mangels, thresh the rustling sheaves, spread the manure. Commodities from potatoes, corn, coal and hay were carried on a range of carts and waggons, often of local composition, which are a lifetime's study in themselves.

Their design was governed by contour and climate. In the Eastern Counties we find huge, rumbling waggons pulled by teams of Shires or Suffolks, leading wheat or barley over often rough but seldom steep tracks in a climate dry enough to allow very large stacks to be built. In the west, Dales, Fell, Highland and Welsh native ponies and cobs would haul smaller carts, often in hilly country and in a high rainfall area. Those capacious, square-ended stacks of more fertile regions were replaced by smaller, round ones, always with a view to defeating the weather. Whether round or square they may, in the early days, have been influenced by religion.

The mid-nineteenth century makes a convenient starting point for a study of horse-drawn farm implements. Any built from then onwards are recognisable as at least akin to those still used today. Vehicles, implements and draught animals from before that date would be less familiar to today's enthusiasts.

Turnpike roads had been a big feature in rural transport, but by the 1870s were on their way out. They were losing ground to the railways, destined to have an important bearing on the spread of machinery. If carts had a broad enough tyre, they could go free on the turnpike roads, as their roller effect helped bind the surface. When that broad tyre width was no longer a factor, cart and waggon designs could and did change.

Turnpike roads were the arterial lifeblood of the agricultural revolution. They may be compared with the German autobahns or our modern motorways. The tolls raised a fund towards road maintenance, but were unpopular, and toll-bars were frequently pulled down and burnt until the 1728 Act made their destruction a felony. They then multiplied rapidly, and from the 1760s they enabled country people in most areas to go to town - even a small market town - in a way previously impossible.

Yet the inequality of the toll-bar burden was strongly felt. 'In one district, five tolls might be paid in 12 miles; in another, 30 might be travelled without a single payment', wrote Lord Ernle in English Farming, Past and Present. 'The financial chaos of the trusts, as well as the inadequacy of the statute labour, gave a fresh impulse to the ultimate triumph of the rival principle of a rate'.

In 1878 the turnpike roads were made main roads, and in 1888 the County Councils took over, relieving parochial districts of their remaining liabilities.

RAILWAYS

The railway system had large and sometimes unexpected effects on farming, and on the horse population in particular. Smallholders hired themselves out with their horses and carts to help build the railways. Railway companies were very big employers of draught horses and of horsemen; the horse population of some centres was bigger than the human one. The place and street names with affinity to horses in big cities illustrate this well; Haymarket and mews are obvious examples.

GRAIN

The flood of cheap grain imports from the New Countries arrived in Britain in the 1870s, resulting in a contraction of the arable acreage in England, with fewer horses and implements needed. In Scotland, the rotation was extended by sowing longer leys, so the cultivated acreage was not diminished in the same way.

AMERICAN INFLUENCE

Coupled with this flood of grain came the start of North American machinery imports. James Oliver emigrated from the Scottish Borders to USA, and set up his own plow works (using the American spelling). He realised the need of the homesteading farmer to be able to obtain a numbered part for his plough, simply by wiring the number and having it delivered by rail, probably on the Rockefeller rail system. Mouldboard, sock, coulter and every part of the different models had its own number.

This numbering system spread to binders and reapers, and put Olivers firmly on the map. Today we take it for granted; at the time it was a huge step forward.

Three other factors combined to take the farm machinery business away from local foundries and into the national network. Without banking, the penny post and the farming Press, these changes could not have happened.

By 1760, paper money was fairly widespread. Only a decade earlier, Robert Burns was sent a bank note by his father, and he and his brother were puzzled as to what to do with it. In the late 18th century, bank managers were known as agents, and it was not until the spread of the banking network that farmers could pay for something ordered from a distance.

POST

The penny post was the means by which these cheques travelled. Sadly, all these innovations coincided with prolonged agricultural depression, a retreat from the 'high farming' methods of the mid-nineteenth century, and one that was to continue with only short breaks until 1939.

PRESS

The farming Press and the weekly local newspaper became available to working farmers in the late nineteenth century. They enabled manufacturers to display details of their goods far afield, rather than simply to farmers who visited the foundry on market days, or who travelled by pony and trap to a works within range.

Advertising took off. We may complain about today's sometimes over-rosy advertisements, but the early ones promoting stock medicines with enticing names were often dealing in quite worthless goods, sheep dips being an exception.

Farm machinery and vehicles could, however, be described to a much wider audience. Then as now, some of the illustrations were rather fanciful, depicting much lighter and swifter horses than would in fact be needed to pull the implements except on the lightest soils, and certainly working on better or more level ground than the norm.

An offshoot of these developments was that national time became necessary. In the eighteenth century, there could be three sets of time in one village; the church clock, the shop clock, and one by a watch belonging to the oldest inhabitant! With the railways' spread, national time became essential, and the engine driver's reliable watch was used to check local variations.

Right up to the end of World War II, a watch was a comparatively expensive piece of equipment, a prize possession. From the eighteenth century, grandfather or long case clocks became status symbols, found in farmers' and tradesmen's houses, never in workers' cottages. Reliance on the railways for time keeping was still a feature of 1930s life, the 'twelve o'clock express' being the signal for dinnertime, the trundling five o'clock goods an indication that knocking-off time was approaching.

From the 1870s, farm implement design remained comparatively static. Even Bell's reaper was of admirable and practical design, its successors resorting to offset draught as the main difference. Changes came gradually, and were generally aimed at reducing weight and draught rather than in fundamental design alterations.

THE GREAT EXHIBITION

One single manifestation that awoke our mid-nineteenth century forebears to the application of machinery was the Great Exhibition of 1851. It had a galvanic effect, not only on town industry but on the countryside. Before it, hand labour held sway. After it, any device for speeding or easing man's labour was applauded. Its direct influence may have been on the landowning and more prosperous tenant farmer classes, but the changed attitudes it inspired affected farming generally.

The urge to mechanise affected the livestock industries. A classic example is Small's plough of c1765 which needed two horses and one man, replacing a much larger team of horses and/or oxen and a boy to guide them. Small's plough resulted in a surge of interest in the breeding of Clydesdale horses, strong, quick-stepping creatures far removed from the ponderous Blacks of Middle England in the eighteenth century.

As horses replaced oxen, triple-purpose cattle disappeared, to be replaced by specialist beef or dairy breeds, and a few dual-purpose. Working oxen were part of the European scene much longer, and today there is a renewed interest in this form of power.

The great surge in pedigree breeding of working horses dated from the late 1870s, when Suffolk, Shire and Clydesdale breeders put pen to paper and began to record their stock's parentage. Until then, that had been the prerogative of the Thoroughbred horse in its General Stud Book, and Coates' Herd Book for Shorthorn cattle. It is no coincidence that the development of machinery was matched by horses able to pull it to best advantage.

'Weight is needed to move weight' was a favoured saying, and Shire and Clydesdale took on massive forms. The Suffolk, then a mainly agricutural animal, was less affected.

That first horse-drawn age lasted little over a century. Before it, oxen held sway; the internal combustion brought it almost to a close in the 1950s. In between, the horse was king, and those tending to its needs formed an appreciable part of the rural population.

The way of life it engendered had many advantages. Self-sufficiency was one; the village joiner and wheelwright on his Sunday afternoon walks would spy an elm, ash or oak growing straight and true in wood or hedgerow, and arrange to buy it, (but not on the Sabbath).

Then in the dead season he and his assistants and apprentices would fell it, lead it home by horse power, perhaps using a timber dray, saw it into planks and make it into that part of cart or waggon which experience had proved the best. He could then tell by his ear if he had made a first-class job, simply by listening to it rumbling down the stoned road.

That seems an over-glamourised version of village life. On the reverse of the coin were the long, hard hours, scant regard for a working man's or lad's welfare, and the lack of money. Wages were low, and apprentices had very little spare cash, but worked all the time for the future.

Wheelwrights have told me how, in their apprentice days, they were tired out through working twelve hours daily up to their knees in shavings. Till these mounds really affected output, or until there was a slack day, no one cleared them away. To do so simply to ease an apprentice's lot was unthinkable, 'encouraging idleness', and idleness was a cardinal sin of that era.

The employers were in little better state. The term 'cash flow' had not been invented. Accounts were sent out quarterly, and in some cases annually, and such was agricultural depression that farmers might be extremely slow in paying. In close-knit communities, patience in waiting for settlement of bills was part of life.

Opposite: *A splendid pair of Suffolks at a ploughing match.*

CHAPTER 2

Ploughs and

Ploughing

Advertisement for Howard ploughs.

Of all man's inventions, the plough has been proved the most useful. It is found in these pages in infinite variety, but all with the same basic concept of turning over the soil while progressing.

The plough. being the fundamental implement of agriculture, is common to all ages and countries, and its primitive form is almost everywhere the same, says Loudon in 1883. The forms used by the Greeks and Romans seem to have spread over Europe, and changed little until about the 16th century. Then English improvements came in the 17th century, with the Scotch plough in the 18th century showing modifications and lightness of form much nearer our present day models.

High-cut or oat-seed furrow is the apex of the horsemen's art, yet the plough that achieves this is no longer used in commercial farming operations. The ploughing match remains with us because an exponent of the high-cut may be deemed master of any other operation involving horses.

The standard plough team in most counties was a pair of horses. For certain fields, three were used, and there is a field of Northamptonshire clay that needed five horses in line to turn a single furrow. Such soils were referred to as 'horse-killing land'.

To plough effectively, horses must be fit, for they have no opportunity for rest or lowered draft once turned into the new furrow.

Ploughing allows what life seldom offers; a new start. Old stubble, new weeds, irregularities, plant diseases and plant food are all turned under by the plough, and there are few satisfactions greater than ploughing straight and true furrows in gold of stubble or green of ley, giving the best possible start to the next crop.

The Society of Ploughmen acknowledges this through its never ending efforts to encourage better ploughing. In the horse age that this book covers, good ploughing was fundamental. Weeds must be buried, for there were no weed sprays to substitute for poor cultivations. Turf and green manure must be turned under at identical depths across the field, for artificial manures in their infancy could not make up for the loss of plant food resulting from bad ploughing.

Only too often, the tractor driver's employer is less interested in quality than quantity of work. He asks 'Has Bob finished that field?', rather than how well he has ploughed it. When standard output was one acre per plough per day, quality of work was really taken into account, for no following imple-ment, spray or fertiliser could retrieve the situation resulting from bad workmanship.

Immediately after harvest - remembering that September was then the harvest month - the plough teams would strain up and down, up and down, in a prodigious effort to have all land ploughed by Christmas.

Ploughing was the fulcrum of the year; if it was late, so was everything else. With today's tractors and multi-furrow ploughs, the operation figures much less in the farmer's thoughts; its accomplishment is almost taken for granted.

Some ploughs are found in the chapter on root harvesting (pp 86). Though their framework is basically the same, they have devices for fitting the crop rather than burying the rubbish. Yet even apart from these, a vast range of ploughs was made as variants from the the general purpose, single furrow.

Multiple-furrows found less favour in Britain than across the seas. They are mostly of the digger or semi-digger type, less satisfying to use, and capable of attracting much more scorn from fellow workers in the days when a gang of young chaps would walk from farm to farm on a Sunday morning, discussing the best and deriding the worst ploughing.

In North America, Australasia and South Africa, such strictures did not apply. Soils were different, often lighter, and so vast that a seat became not only desirable but essential. In Britain pre-1950, the surviving old-time foremen abhorred seats as 'encouraging idleness', a cardinal sin.

To walk behind a pair of Suffolks, Shires or Clydesdales to a single furrow plough was one thing, to drive a mass of 'half-legged' (light x heavy horse) animals quite another. With those big teams, the lead horses were the key, and the rest packed in behind, relying on the herd instinct, minimum handling and a certain amount of luck to take the multi-furrow from one end of the field to the other. In Britain, where skilled men were plentiful, there was not the same incentive to save labour that would be needed at other seasons anyway.

In a tight-knit village community, few farmers relished putting a good man 'on the dole' through no fault of his own. So the single furrow and pair of horses remained the standard, with ingenious variations to suit different soils.

Drainage ploughs were specialist models designed to work at greater than normal depths, as was the sub-soil plough. These really were hard on the horses, and horsemen, fond of their teams, would find reasons why they were not practical. The tractor has come to the horse's aid and made feasible such mechanical means of deeper cultivation.

One other plough must be mentioned: the snow plough. Here again it would be idle to pretend that horses were superior to mechanised methods, for the simple reason that no matter how strong and willing the team, they had to breast the drifts themselves before they could push the snow to one side, and this in itself required a massive effort.

One of the great names of plough design and manufacture was Ransomes Sims & Jefferies, Ltd. From their Orwell Works, Ipswich, they produced a huge range of ploughs to suit any type of soil, at home or abroad. From the edge of the East Anglian arable they sent skilled ploughmen and ploughs to the three corners of the British Isles, and backed up sales with a well-organised spare parts network. Their experience goes back to the reign of King George III. 1760-1820)

Above *The Passing Shower, Haltwhistle, Northumberland.*

Ransomes Newcastle range of general purpose ploughs covers eight types, varying from 287lb to 336 lb. The standard fitting is with two wheels, long beam, short handles, cast breast of medium length and knife coulter.

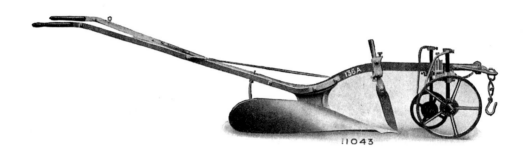

Ransomes Yorkshire ploughs are strong and efficient, easy to handle, light in draught. They are claimed to be specially designed for Yorkshire, though as the County of Broadacres includes every type of farming known throughout the UK, this smacks of a sales ploy. Subsoiling, sugar beet lifting and mole draining attachments are extras.

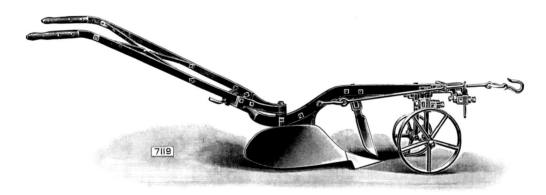

The Fruita plough was specially designed for cultivating close up to fruit trees and bushes. Handles are mounted on a special bracket, and combined with the draught arrangement allows the ploughman to walk clear of the trees while guiding the plough.

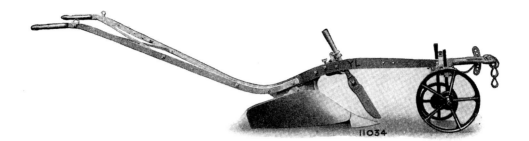

The Trussed Beam Plough turns a furrow from four to nine inches deep and from nine to twelve inches wide. It is light enough for two horses and strong enough for four. An Open Frame version is designed to supersede the old wood plough, and had an open frame and high coupling.

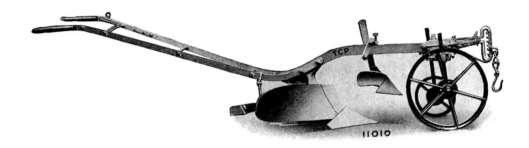

Steel Chill Digging ploughs turned a furrow up to twelve inches wide, leaving the soil thoroughly pulverised. They were ideal for stubble ploughing and cross ploughing, moulding up hops and deep ploughing in the market garden. Their ability to bury twitch and weeds take us back to pre-weed spraying days. Skim coulters were standard, set between the mouldbard and wheels

Above: *Where it was necessary to skim off virtually the full width of the furrow, Ransomes provided a special skim coulter. When old pastures were ploughed, the skimmed surface was place in the furrow bottom. Fine setting was needed, for if set too deep a large skim could bring a pair of horses to its knees.*

Farmers lucky enough to possess great depth of soil
sometimes wished to bring up fresh soil to the surface,
for which the deep digging plough was designed. It
ploughed to a depth of 14 inches, completely turning
over a furrow 16 to 18 inches wide, and had a 28-
inches furrow wheel and cranked crossbar. A 32-inches
furrow wheel was also available, as was a Mole
Draining attachment.

The Irish pattern Special Lea Plough was designed for
high cut work especially on lea and old grassland. It
seems designed to play to local patriotism, as did the
Lancashire and Cheshire ploughs, rather than to any
design improvements.

The Galloway digging plough was introduced for use
on stony land in the South of Scotland, and the
Gudekut for the Highlands.

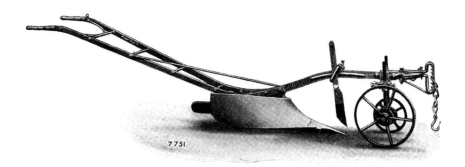

The Guidtop plough was designed for Scottish districts where the furrow was set up to leave a 'guid top'. It has a sabre point pattern instead of the bar point of the Gudekut.

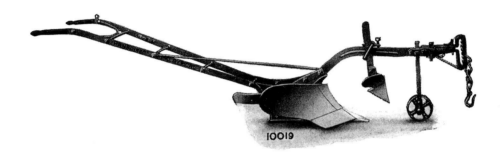

The No. 2 Claymore was specially built for Scotland where a wide bottom and broken furrow was required. It was fitted with chilled breast and share, malleable frame and cast chilled slade with a wide flange. Its reversible cast chilled point was claimed to have double the usual life.

The one-horse or light two-horse ploughs were suitable for light or medium soils, and ploughed a furrow from four to seven inches deep. A Small Holdings model ploughed within the capacity of a pony or light horse.

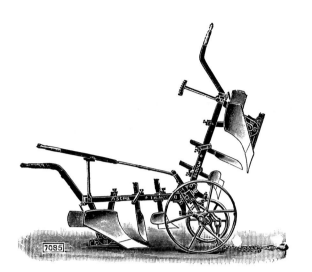

Balance ploughs, as in this deep digging model, obviated the need to set rigs. The ploughman started on one straight side, and continued right across the field till he reached the far boundary.

The Turnabout plough differs from the Balance plough in that the plough bodies or breasts swung around the frame by pressing down a pedal. This is plough weighed 264 lb.

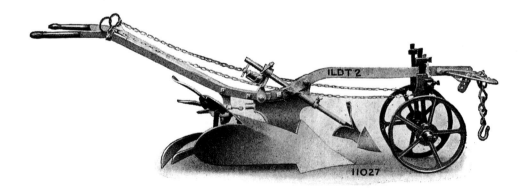

In the swivel One Way plough, the furrows could be laid either to the right or to the left. Snap wheel fastenings from the handles allowed the wheels to act alternately as land or furrow wheels.

Ransome's double furrow plough Y.L.D.A. with Bowl Land Wheel

Howard's Wholeroot-R beet lifter, mole drainer and subsoiler. The mole drainer made a small circular tunnel to help drainage, while the subsoiler broke up the 'pan' liable to form on some soils where ploughing depths remained unaltered for many years.

The Grampian swing ridging plough was designed primarily for Scotland, and could be fitted with two types of breast. It was often possible to fit a fan of tines for potato lifting. Width of work altered by a screw adjuster. Ploughing 'swing' means ploughing without wheels, a difficult art as the plough point might bury itself, but one easier in the hands of a skilled operator.

Left: *Howard plough*

Above: *Oliver digger plough lacking share, coulter and wheels. Many thousands were imported in the 1930s, and were very popular on light land.*

A blacksmith-made Devon reversible plough, demonstrated by John Peacock at the Royal Show 2000. Terry Keegan's well known Heavy Horse Enthusiast stand is in the background.

Richard Coot won the Wormside match, Herefordshire. Here he is with Roger Lewis, who made one thousand gallons of cider every year, all consumed on the farm!

"Land of the mountain and the flood."

Above: *Here's some nice soil bordering a Scottish loch. Note the peaked collars, and these 1907 horses that appear chestnut, unlike modern Clydesdales.*

Below: *This is a very large and deep furrow. Witness the need for five horses all of whom keep their feet in the furrow. (Jersey).*

Above: *Richard Coot nearing the end of his plough-ing stint with his black Shires.*

Left: *A genuine pair of working horses. Judging by the hat, the ploughman is Tom Cliff!*

Right: *A turn-wrest plough at the French horse breeding station of Le Haras du Pin.*

Left: *A Warwickshire match plough, drawn by Donald J Smith.*

Left: *An interesting eighteenth century wheeless plough by Donald J Smith.*

Left: *Details of a Kent plough by Donald J. Smith*

Below: *Waiting to Work, by Malcolm Coward. Sally Mitchell reproduces this 18 x 24 inches oil on canvas as a greetings card.*

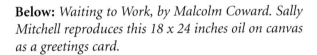

151. The make-up of the big teams was scientifically studied in North America. 'Tying in' and 'bucking back' were methods of keeping control over the large numbers. A run-away with such a team was a serious event. Other than the leaders, these horses were seldom broken in the British sense; they were packed in with little finesse. The driver kept a container of stones to sling at any laggards. Lamarr Bontrager is ploughing with 12 Belgians in Indiana, USA

Harrows

Cultivating

and Rolling

Fig. 44.—Cross

Above: *Rolling knobbly land in Essex. Note the smoother soil after only one pass of the roller.*

HARROWS

Harrowing heavy arable can be especially hard work. The big clods are very tiring for both horses and drivers, who stumble along as best they can. Modern athletes prone to ankle injuiries should spend a few days following a pair of smart-stepping Clydesdales over newly-ploughed clay!

We shall see how harrows are needed for a whole range of tasks, from breaking down heavy clay to dispersing droppings on grassland.

I have harrowed using the primitive method with strong thorns. The field in question was far from home, its hedge had been newly laid, so there were masses of hawthorn branches around. A selection was laid in a deep row and a five-bar field gate tied on top to weight them down. Ropes tied through the bars and back to the strongest thorns were led to the cobbletree, and off we went. Dung pats were spread effectively, tufts of rough grass pulled out, and the end result was a series of pretty light and dark green stripes!

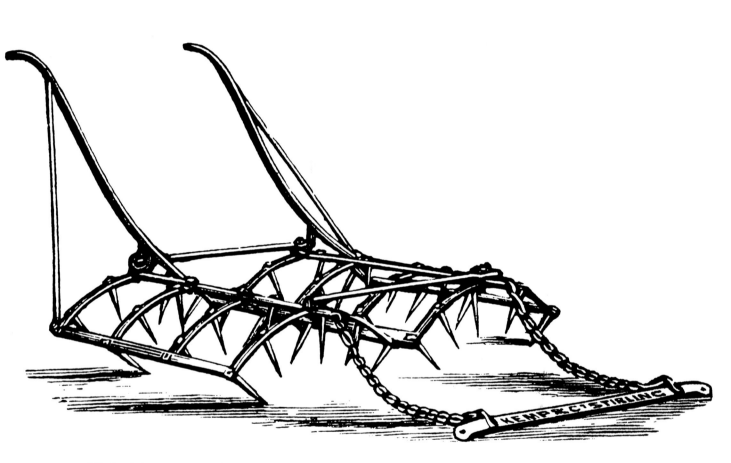

Saddle back harrows to pull the small rubbish on potato rows before the plants emerge. Some days later, the ground will be rowed up again.

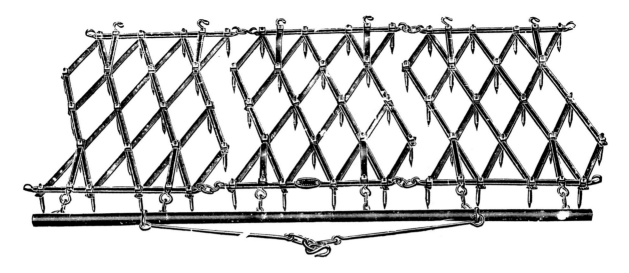

How a harrow is constructed.

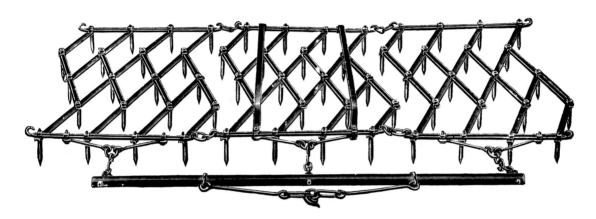

These harrows are for preparing the seedbed.

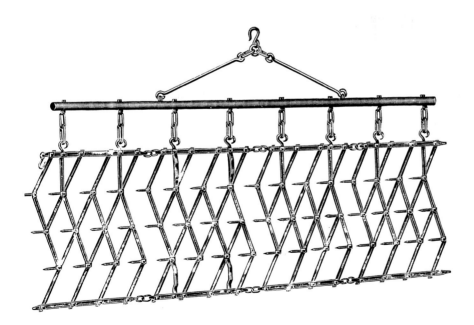

Light seed harrows for covering the seed after drilling.

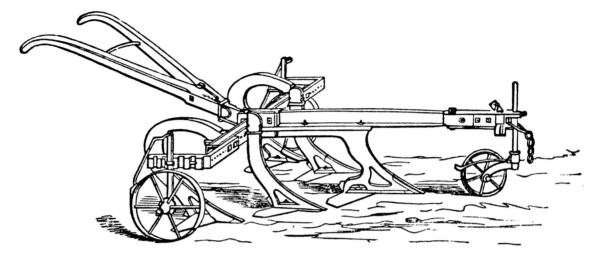

Fig. 46.—Bentall's Grubber.

Here we have different types of early cultivator. Bentall's Grubber (above) and Coleman's cultivator were for preliminary work on a strong land seedbed, or for getting in deep during summer fallow to drag wickens or couch grass to the top.

Fig. 47.—Coleman and Son's Patent Cultivator.

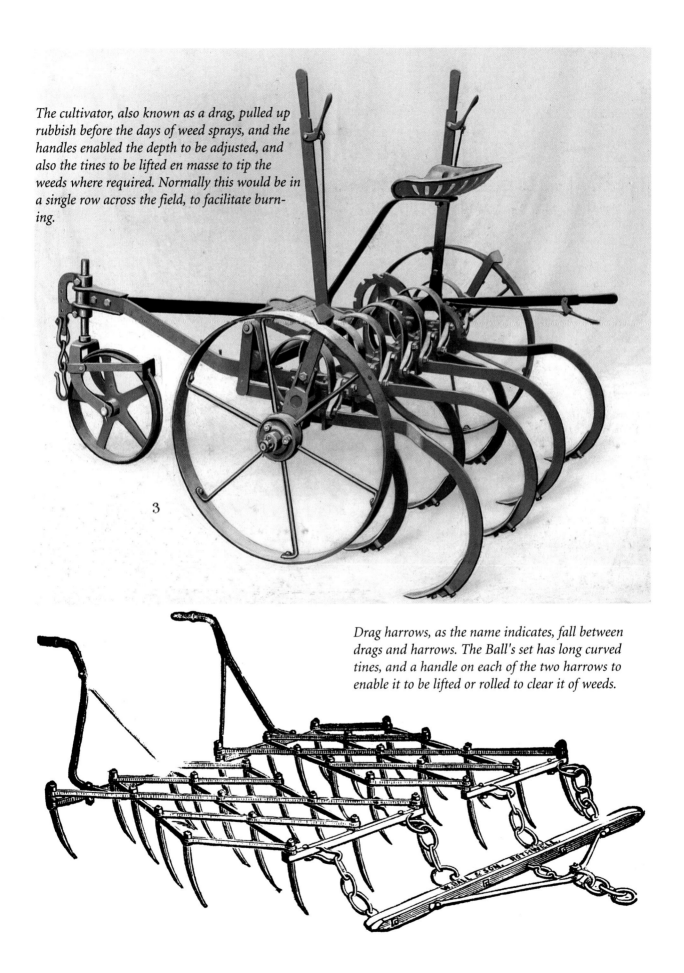

The cultivator, also known as a drag, pulled up rubbish before the days of weed sprays, and the handles enabled the depth to be adjusted, and also the tines to be lifted en masse to tip the weeds where required. Normally this would be in a single row across the field, to facilitate burning.

3

Drag harrows, as the name indicates, fall between drags and harrows. The Ball's set has long curved tines, and a handle on each of the two harrows to enable it to be lifted or rolled to clear it of weeds.

Saddle-back harrows are for harrowing down ridges. Potatoes were usually set in ridges, and in pre-weed spray days pulling down the ridges helped weed control. For turnips, mangels and sugar beet, the ridge gave somewhere to pull the rubbish when hoeing.

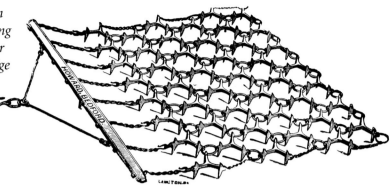

Spiked chain harrows were also useful in gathering weeds brought to the surface by drag or cultivator. Cylindrical, horizontal Weights attached to their rear kept them to their job, and could be used as handles to lift the harrow when filled with weeds. Weeds were rolled into swathes for later collection.

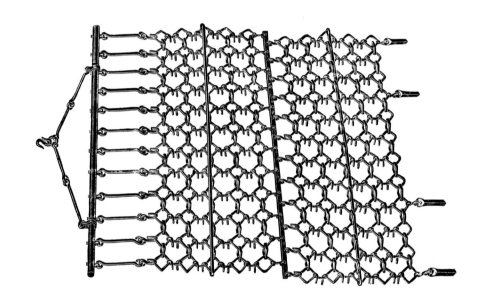

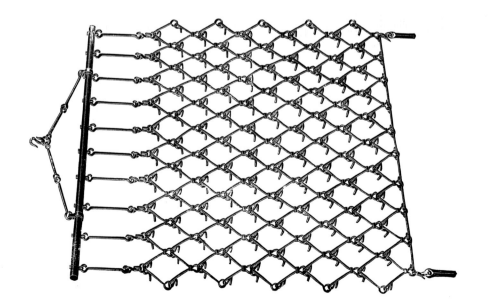

The Flexible Tine Harrow is specially suitable for grass, though it too can roll up weeds on arable. It has been shown that grass harrowing is one job in which a team of active horses can still compete with and match a tractor pricewise, and operate in a wet spring when tractors might make too much of a mess on the land.

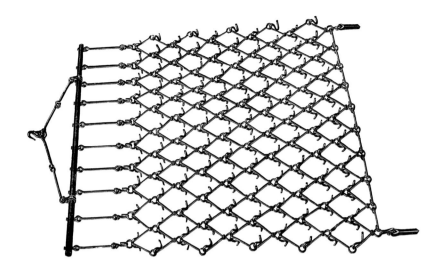

Double tined flexible harrows have short tines on one side and longer ones on the other. They can thus suit the various kinds of work needed, with the short tines having a lower draught on smooth grassland, while the longer ones can break up mole hills or scatter manure.

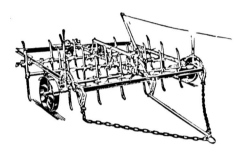

The pitch-pole harrow is well named. The pointed tines pitch into the soil, and are driven in and then turned over by the forward movement of the implement. It is a dual purpose implement which takes the place of a drag harrow for arable land and also acts as a grassland renovator. It possesses double-ended tines, and a knife-edged pattern is employed when the harrow is used for tearing old turf and aerating pasture. If the knives gather trash they can be cleared by allowing them to revolve or 'pitch-pole'. Three transport wheels are provided; the depth is set by hand levers, and the pitching action controlled by a cord to the trip lever.

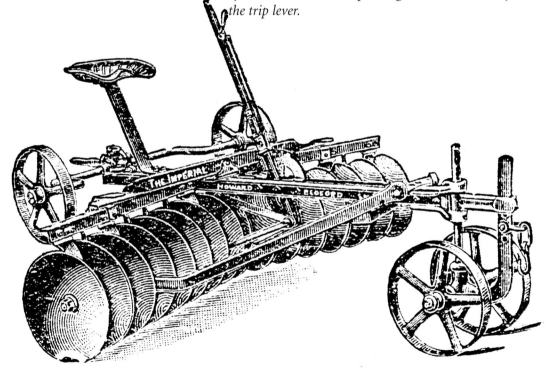

In Britain the disc harrow was seldom a horseman's favourite. The reason is that even a slight alteration in the set of the discs can result in greatly increased draught, and almost bring a pair of horses to its knees. More than three horses constituted a big team for cultivations in the pre-tractor era and the horsemen were unwilling to impose too great a strain on their charges.

A set of disc harrows consists of
two gangs of discs attached to a
framework that carries the shaft
and the driver's seat. The gangs
are hinged, and their angle varied
by ratchet lever according to the
`nature of the work required. The
machine's balance is maintained
as the drag from one set is counter-
balanced by the drag from the
other, curved in the opposite direction. Discs do not clog, a big
advantage, but straight-tooth harrows are needed to make a seed
bed after them. For moving, they
are raised on wheels.

Dick Brown discing soya bean stubble with his eight Percherons at Heritage Farm, Hudson, Iowa. The 13-feet tandem disc is followed by four black Percherons drilling oats with a John Deere drill. (photo Bob Mischka)

Inter-row cultivators were for cleaning between rows of root crops. Martin's machine took three rows at a time, and doubles as a ridger by fitting double breasts.

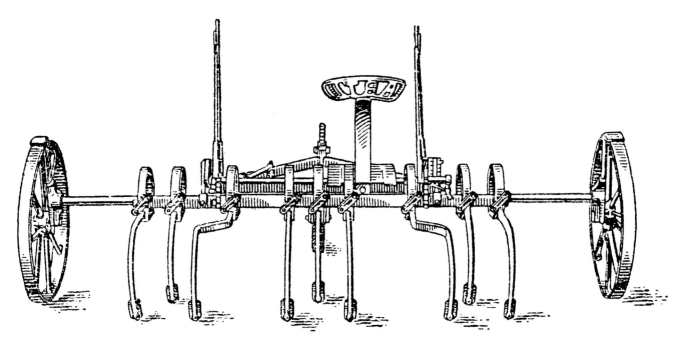

Martin's machine as 3-drill grubber

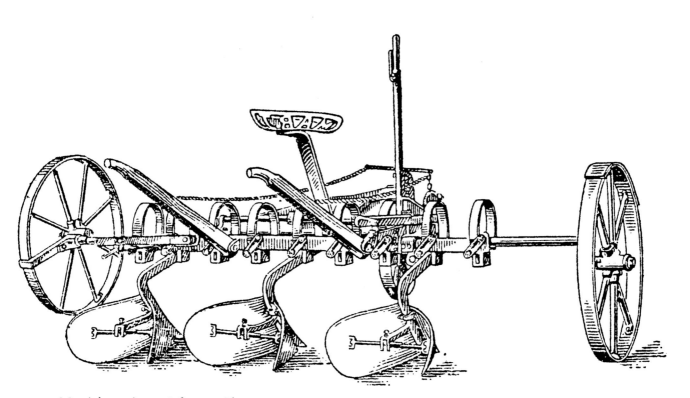

Martin's macine as 3-furrow ridger

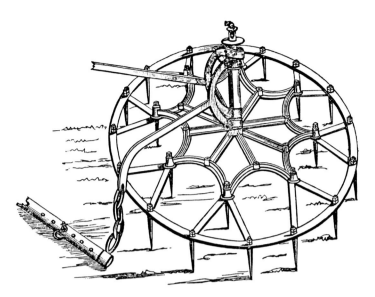

Circular harrows appear to have been designed in an attempt to initiate perpetual motion.. They never became popular, but modern tractor implements seek to imitate them, as the rotary motion is more easily powered from a tractor.

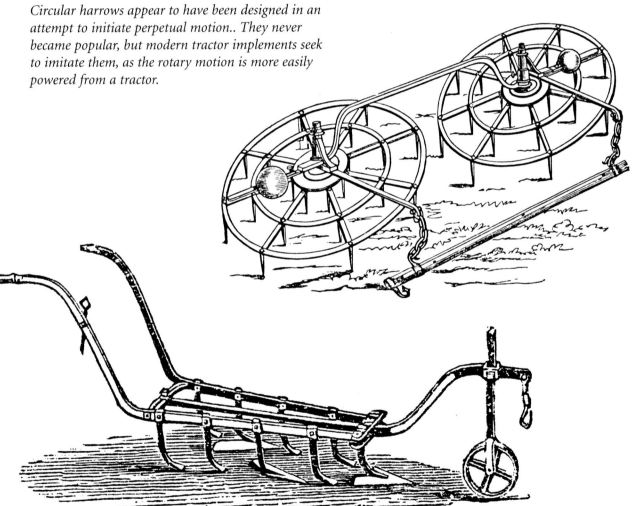

The single-row scruffler was used the first time over, before the crop was singled. A skilled horseman could lighten the hoers' work by shaving close to the plants with the protective discs fitted at that stage.

ROLLERS

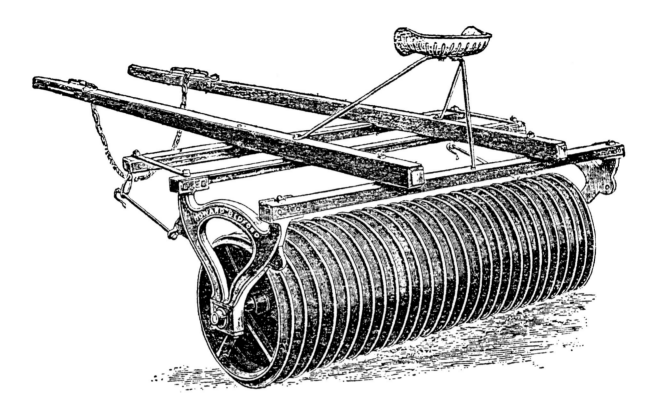

Most rollers are made of iron, and are split into a series of cylinders to facilitate turning at the ends. The most extreme form is the Cambridge roller, which consists of narrow, heavily rimmed segments along a central axle. This Howard version has a seat, but most were a 'walking job'. It reminds me of trying to cope with some 'Stittenham clay' just away from the Vale of York, where the Cambridge roller was bouncing on the hard knots. I suggested to The Boss (my uncle) that I fix a seat on to give more weight. 'Fill some bags with sand and walk', he abjured. 'You'll expect to be paid for doing nowt (nothing) next!' Worker comfort was never a priority in the horse days.

Above: *A view in perspective of a turnip-drill contrived by Mr. Geddes, Cargen Bridge, Dumfriesshire. Its construction of parts is much the same as that already described, but the depression of the parts forming the framework gives the machine an appearance of compactness and strength.*

Below: *A flat roller or plain roller had just two segments as a rule, and was useful in leaving a smooth surface on finely harrowed plough land just before drilling. Rolling is more effective when done slowly; bumping a set along behind a tractor is less beneficial than with the horse's steady pace. This is proved when you come to a wet patch, and are afraid of becoming bogged down. Driving through quickly decreases the draught; the implement is much more likely to become stuck at a slow pace.*

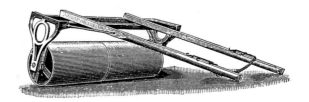

A furrow press is a special type of roll, and is used straight after ploughing. The wedge-shaped rims bear down into the furrow grooves, and are adjustable..

Donald J Smith's version of a single-horse press; note the land wheel which keeps the axle horizontal.

Below: *Yoking to two single-horse rollers.*   **Above and Opposite top:** *Clod crushers.*

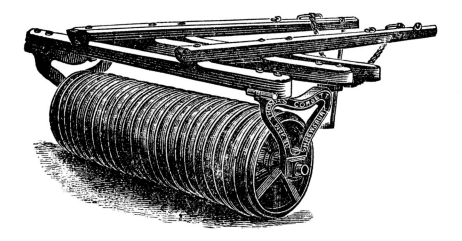

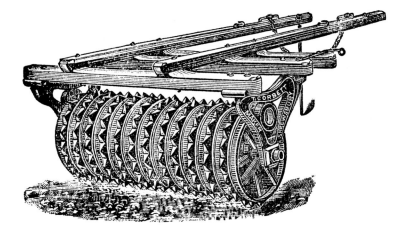

Below: *Stone rollers are of necessity quite small, as they are very heavy. Naturally they are more common in quarrying areas. Their small diameter makes them very penetrating, There was a very good one used to roll the cricket pitch at Spout House, Bilsdale, North Yorkshire, but some merry lads rolled it from the top of the field to the bottom during royal celebrations, chipping a piece off which necessitated dressing down the circumference.*

Below: *Joe Godderidge farms in Norfolk and his six Shire crosses provide nearly all the power on the land. They also serve to model for the paintings which are usually a direct reflection of his own life.*

Above: *A one horse roller at a Countryside Cavalcade, note the metal frame and tubular metal shafts.*

Below: *Rolling knobbly land in Essex. Note the smoother soil after only one pass of the roller.*

An Essex Spring Working, with a Shire pair pulling a spring-tined cultivator, and a drill in the background.

Seeding

and

Weeding

Fig. 44.—Cross

Robert Eddy driving a straight drill line.

Drilling machines have a long and chequered story. Attempts were made quite early in agricultural history to give more precision to this vital operation, but were frustrated, often by labour opposition. Then developments came, to prove so fundamentally sound that they have remained basically the same for a century and more.

Chinese, Japanese and Indian husbandmen almost certainly drilled or dibbled their seed, the ancient Chinese method being a wheelbarrow arrangement leaving three shallow furrows in the soil. The ancient Sumerians attached a seed dropper to the plough beam; a similar device did not arrive in Europe until the late eighteenth century.

In 1566 the Venetian Camillo Torello invented a seed drill, and later that century Tadeo Cavalini of Bologna produced another seemingly efficient drilling machine. In England, a number of seed drills were patented after 1623, as described in contemporary books and literature, but do not seem to have been produced commercially.

Even in 1669, inventors were trying to combine the sowing of seed simultaneously with dry manure, especially pigeon droppings which were plentiful at that time. John Worlidge in his Systema Agriculturae described a seed dropping method that proved an important development. Its wooden wheel had a number of leather flaps or pockets around the rim, which was belt-driven from the rear wheel axle to revolve in the bottom of a seed hopper. The flaps caught up the seeds, and delivered them into the mouth of a curved discharge funnel as the wheel turned over. This was a primitive force-feed drill, later made with a fluted or spirally

Sowing, harrowing and rolling at Hedley Hill Farm, Cornsay, Co. Durham.

Single horse turnip drill, and a man hoeing.

grooved roller to ensure a regular stream. However, when Professor Bradley constructed a machine from Worlidge's drawings, it did not work.

A German, Locatelli, shortly afterwards invented the precursor of the spoon or cup-feed drill destined to be universally used throughout Europe. In his drill, the seed dropper was contained in a separate compartment at the bottom of a hopper, and was formed by small metal spoons fixed in four rows along a cylinder or axle. Yet this device does not seem to have progressed beyond a limited circle.

Jethro Tull was born at Basildon in 1674. He was the son of a Berkshire landowner and, despite ill health and an antagonistic set of labourers, produced a drill that delivered seed through notched barrels at even depth. A bush harrow to cover the seed trailed behind. The methods of inter-row cultivations that were made possible were even more important than the drill itself. Hoeing or pulling rubbish was at that time the only means of weed control. Tull's drill enabled a horse hoe to be used, greatly assisting and cutting down labour.

Tull died in 1764, after which his work seems to have lain unrecognised for some years. Then certain Scottish farmers revived his ideas, and between 1780 and 1790 thirteen patents were obtained for seed-sowing machines. Next came a decade with no patents, followed by a surge of interest and a range of different types before 1830.

By 1860 the Suffolk drill as made by Smyth of Peasenhall was brought practically to its present form. It was furnished with cup feed, rocking hopper, chain and roller lift and compression, hoe coulters and a special steerage arrangement. More than two horses were usual, driven by one man while the other steered the drill.

The other modern type is more compact, with lever lift, spring compression, force feed and double or single disc coulters. It is driven and operated by one man and drawn by two horses.

Root drills were usually cup-fed, and often combined with manure drilling. The desirability of placing the manure close to the growing crops, though not actually touching the seed, was

recognised early. For root drilling on the flat, no roller was generally provided. On the ridge, a smooth concave roller leads the coulter and a smaller one follows it.

MANURE DISTRIBUTORS

The first broadcast drill for artificial manures came around 1840. The ideal machine should be able to sow any artificial evenly at any rate from half a cwt to 10 or 12 cwt per acre.

Several difficulties had to be overcome. Rough, knotty arable caused greater vibration and therefore heavier sowing than smooth grass. Metal working parts suffered corrosion, while manures like superphosphate tended to become pasty and clog the works. The rate of sowing could vary as the machine goes up or down hill, a stricture that applied even more to sowing by hand.

In the very early twentieth century, an inverted cone was slung between the two ground wheels, and manure was fed onto a horizontal disc rotating at high speed. A different kind imported from Central Europe before 1914 had an endless chain working the length of the drill, whereas the British version had rollers working on the opposite direction to the land wheels to carry a stream of manure to the ground. I have seen both these types put away carelessly though apparently clean, only for moisture from the atmosphere to make the working parts a sticky mess, and often ruined after only two or three years.

Sowing by hand; two teams harrowing in.

A flat roller pulled by a light grey horse. Sowing oats by hand, 1900.

Mr Moffitt sowing corn with six-abreast team, Saskatchewan, Canada 1928-29.

A cup feed drill of the late nineteenth century. The feed mechanism may be clearly seen , as is the drive wheel activated by the offside land wheel. These drive wheels were interchangeable with smaller or larger ones, according to the sowing rate. Eight-coulter drills such as this were soon superseded by bigger ones.

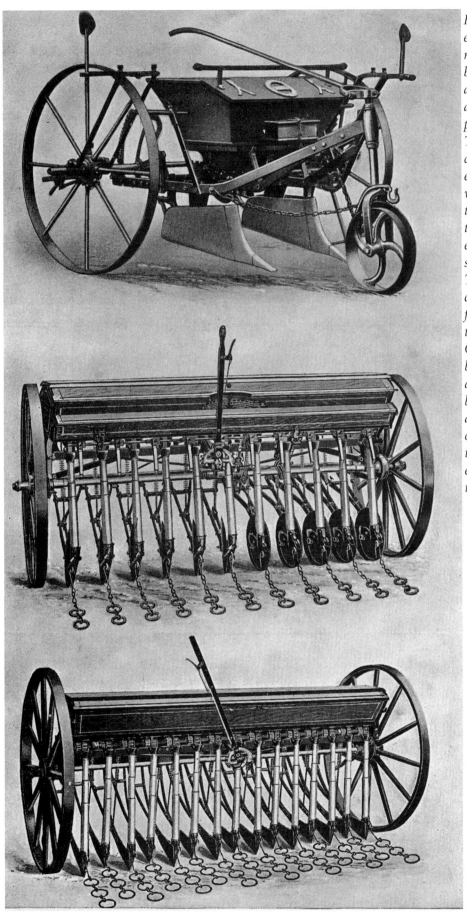

Here are three early twentieth century models. The top-
most drill, Wallace's combined Double Drill Plough
and Manure distributor, fed
artificial manures into the
potato rows being formed.
The centre disc drill cut a
channel for the seed, and was
equivalent to an extra cultivation, but it was hard on
the horses. Note the links on
this drill that trail behind
each coulter to smooth the
soil.
The shoe drill has fifteen
coulters, and the cogs which
force-feed the seed corn into
the coulters are clearly seen.
Once when riding the foot-
board of a tractor-drawn
drill, I decided to save time
by oiling the cogs while
drilling was in progress. The
oil can spout was caught by
the cogs and disappeared, to
emerge as a series of serra-
tions.

In Wisconsin, was this pair of American Creams, Jim and Beauty. They will be unfamiliar to British readers.

A Belgian pair (right) and a pair of black Percherons drilling grain at a Wisconsin Draft Horse and Mule Association Field Day.

Paul Birdsall with Bonnie and Mayday furrowing and marking a field which will be planted with potatoes

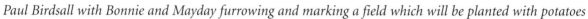

Cyril Eddy drilling corn in Cornwall. Drilling is a difficult art. The Reverend David Nixon as a youth was instructed by his foreman to look well ahead when steering the team. In dry conditions it was sometimes difficult to discern the previous wheel mark, which had to be followed exactly. The foreman was scathing; they usually were. 'You an' yer 'zig-zag, zig-zag. Yer damned nigh crippled all the hares in Creation. Kip a long line, an' yer head up. An' allus, allus, look to the end of the field'.

Crosskill's Water carts are included in this section as they sometimes doubled as liquid manure carts. The body of this Crosskill's cart is made of cast-iron plates, securely cemented and bolted together for holding water or liquid manure, and fitted with a simple brass outlet valve and lever so arranged that a man can open and shut it as he walks by the side of the horse. This cart was extensively used by agriculturists for distributing liquid manure or water by means of a spread board, fixed to the back of the cart.

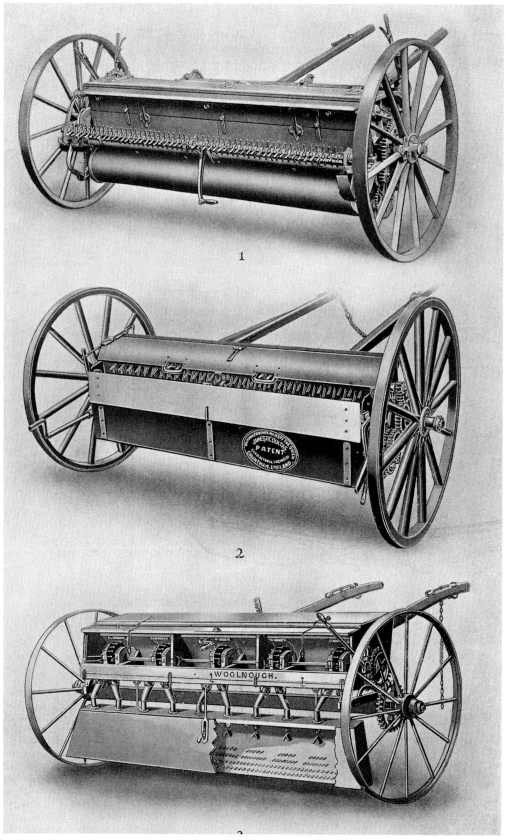

Artificial manure spreaders were developed alongside seed drills, and sometimes in conjunction with them. Three drills of the early 1900s are shown here. Most artificials are heavy and unpleasant to handle, so there was positive incentive to mechanise the process.

Another cart with portable pump and hose pipe as extras. The body of this cart is constructed of wrought-iron or mild steel plates, and afterwards galvanized. It is fitted with a simple brass outlet valve, which can be readily opened and shut by means of a lever on the shaft. It has a spread-board 6-ft long suspended at the back for distributing liquid manure. It was available with wood or wrought iron wheels.

Crosskill's two-wheeler with either wood or wrought- iron wheels. Crosskills also catalogues a similar cart fitted with a good second-hand wine cask.

Crosskill's four wheel farm water cart. Mounted on cast-iron wheels. The body is made entirely of wrought-iron plates, well riveted together and fitted with manhole and tap complete.

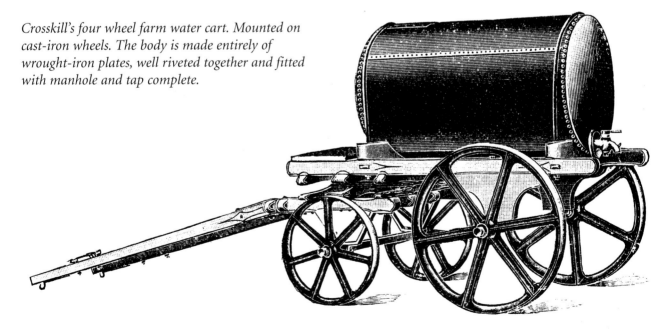

The Four Oaks potato and charlock sprayer with pump suitable for spraying fruit trees also.

A pair of Belgian geldings, Prince and Charlie, drilling in Kentucky. Bobbie Pinkston drives his home-bred pair.

Cyril Eddy drilling with his Shire pair in Cornwall. Robert Eddy (son) and Jane harrowing in background.

Two lively Shires hauling either a grass seed or a fertiliser drill in Essex.

A coulter drill with the coulters jacked up in transport position.

A four-row root drill. A steady horse is a great advantage for this job. On its accuracy depends the ease and effectiveness of inter-row cultivations.

A steady pair drilling corn at an Essex Shire Horse Association work-in.

The drill drawbar rests on a pair of wheels.

A broadcasting machine for bulky materials

An early sprayer at the East of England

Front view of the same machine.

Haymaking

Reapers, Tedders, Turners, Horse Rakes,
Sweeps, Stackers

Haymaking in July 1900. This comes from a scrapbook.

The Birkett family haymaking with a wing sweep. This simple implement is an improvement on using a five-barred gate flat on the ground with a horse at either side. Use of the sweep was only feasible where hay was stacked in the field. It meant harder work at the stack unless an elevator was available, as the hay had to be forked up from the ground rather than from the cart or waggon floor.

'Horses used to have a summer holiday' said Uncle Arthur. He was born in 1850, lived to be 95, and recalled the days when he and his brother Harry scythed five acres of South Pennines meadow in two days. This tremendous feat was not done for the sake of the future agricultural writers, but so they could take their girls to Scarborough on the third day!

The first horse-drawn moving machines arrived in the 1870s. Such innovations were slow to spread, especially to upland farms where cash was always short.

No one has summed up the object of haymaking better than Henry Stephens in 'Book of the Farm' published in 1891.

The converting of fresh grasses and clovers into hay by the drying influences of the sun and wind is an operation of great importance to the British farmer.

OBJECT OF HAYMAKING

Haymaking is the handmaid of stock-rearing. As stock-rearing increases or diminishes, so in all probability will haymaking. Haymaking is the means by which the farmer endeavours to preserve for the winter feeding of his stock the class of food which they pick up for themselves on the fields in summer. The quality and feeding value of this preserved grass much depend upon the manner in which it has been transformed from the green to the dry condition. It is thus of the utmost importance that the process of haymaking should be conducted on the best method known and attainable. We say "attainable," because in our precarious climate the best-laid schemes of farmers are often upset by tantalising outbreaks of unfavourable weather.

WEATHER AND HAYMAKING

Haymaking is peculiarly subservient to climatic conditions. It goes without saying that hay cannot be made in wet weather. Even the proverbial injunction to "make hay while the sun shines" is not without limitation. By the too industrious "making" of hay, under clear scorching sunshine, the quality of the food may be considerably impaired. To expose the fresh grass to such drying influences as will preserve it with the least possible loss in its bulk and nutriment necessitates the exercise of the utmost skill and care.

It is therefore desirable that the various methods of haymaking pursued in different parts of the country should be discussed fully.

All moving machines depend on sharp knifes for efficient work. The cutter bar should be as near level as possible, for if part dips into the ground the edge is taken off. Similarly mole hills are a reapers nightmare. Tiny harvest mice, which build a nest just at the height where the points pick them up, are another obstruction, but nothing much can be done about them.

Two reapers can keep one man sharpening full time. An early device was made by Harrison, McGregor & Co, Leigh, Lancashire. It worked on a tradle, but does not seem to have become very widespread. Perhaps the older men who usually wielded a file to sharpen the knife were content with their usual hand method.

Walter J Malden in the early 1900s told us:

The mower has been subjected to little alteration for some years, and whilst the reciprocating knife passing through a series of slotted fingers is used, there is little likelihood of much change being made. Whether any other form of cutting will ever be found to supersede it is doubtful, though not impossible; for, excellent as the work is, there is the objection that the fingers are somewhat given to block sufficiently to make the knives run hard. The mower frame is always carried on a pair of driving wheels. The cutter bar carrying the knife is loosely hinged to the frame so as to give it freedom to rise and fall with the inequalities of the surface, therefore two travelling wheels are required to balance it.

As the wheels are ordinarily both used for driving purposes, and as at the ends, or when working on a crooked side, these two wheels do not travel at the same pace, and as it is necessary that the knives are kept cutting to clear their way, each one is fitted with a ratchet.

The motion of the knife is imparted from the travelling wheel by a rim gear, a nave gear, or an axle gear, some makers preferring one and some another; and as grass land rarely 'licks up' as does arable land when wet, the objection to the rim gear does not obtain with the mower as it does with

Opposite: *Martin's advertisement for three separate haymaking machines and two gadgets.*

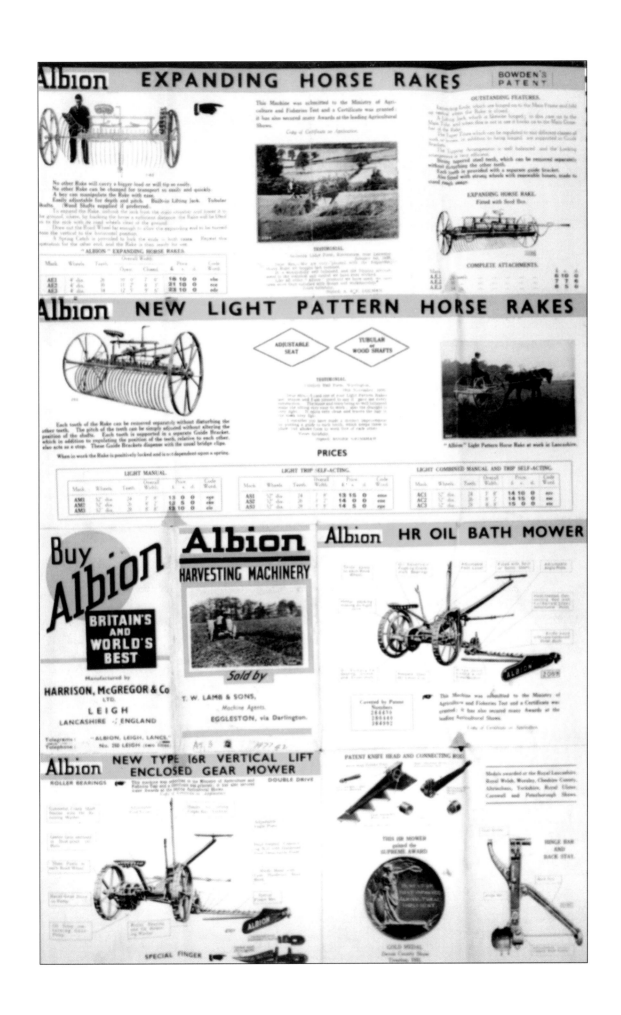

Pike bogey at Low Horsleyhope Farm. This is an early form of low loader. The bogey was tipped to allow the pike to be winched on board.

A pair of horses pulling a rulley. Note the stretcher which keeps the chains from rubbing the trace horse's hind legs. When not needed on the empty return journey, the stretcher was hung on the trace horse's hames.

corn-harvesting machines, where the gear is liable to block with mud. Whichever gear is adopted, the aim is to get the connecting-rod to drive as nearly as possible in a line with the cutter bar.

Modern machines are fitted with suitable levers to allow knives to be quickly raised away from ant-heaps or other obstacles which may suddenly appear in the track; also to alter the pitch of the knives, by changing the relative position of the draught pole to the frame. Ordinarily, mowing machines are not fitted with a revolving reel to bring the grass to the knives, and to keep them clear so that they do not cut the grass again and again. These are used on all corn binders. The difficulty of working the reel from the ordinary gearing of the mower is the reason; and it is due to the fact that the frame and the cutter bar work independently. It was solved by Saunderson, of Bedford, who obtained the Royal Agricultural Society's medal at Leicester for a mower reel worked by an independent travelling wheel attached to the driving pole, thus obtaining the motion required. This can be attached to any mowing machine, and is adjustable to any crop, short or tall, whether standing uptight or leaning away from the advancing knives. Considerably lower cut is thus obtained, and it is not necessary, as is often the case in heavy crops, to have a man with a rake to keep the knives clear.

As the knives of the mowing machine necessarily work very closely to the ground, the sections are liable to be broken or blunted by stones or other substance offering resistance; emery grindstones of suitable shape are the best sharpeners, although files are commonly used. Knife sections injured beyond temporary sharpening have to be removed, work which was tedious with the cold chisel and hammer; but during the last year or two a section remover has been introduced by Eddington & Co. which received the Royal Agricultural Society of England's medal, which has rendered the removal very easy. By taking advantage of the hard steel of the section, the section is made to shear through the soft metal of the rivet; thus by applying a suitably constructed hand tool to the section, with one sharp blow from the hammer the section is removed.

Despite regular sharpening, some blades or sections break or bend beyond repair. The "quickwork" section remover developed by George Henderson speeded blade replacements, and riveted in the new section.

The rotary hay-maker or tedder, with forward and back action, has been for many years generally used in the hayfield to ted or spread out the grass, and it greatly lessened the amount of manual labour. The forward action carried the grass under the machine, up and over, submitting it to very rough treatment, breaking the stalks and so rendering it very susceptible to rain. The back action was less destructive, but when the crop was heavy, it did not effect the work as well as was desired.

The kicker tedder gained much popularity within the past twenty years because of its light draught, and the gentle but effective treatment to which it submitted the grass; and so far as tedding is concerned it leaves little to be desired. The principle of tedding has, however, several objectionable features: it tends to shake out the valuable clovers and tender blades of grass, which are not caught up by the horse rake subsequently; it covers all ground and prevents the drying of the grass; a crop thrown out by the tedder lies beyond the control of the farmer when rain comes, and there is no position in which it can be so thoroughly wetted and spoiled. Moreover, tedded hay is mainly dependent upon sun drying, as air cannot circulate through it freely, and undoubtedly it is highly advantageous to take every advantage of wind drying at every stage in haymaking.

The horse rake becomes almost essential as a collector when grass is tedded. Grass collected by the horse rake is packed and wadded very closely, and unfortunately the damper parts are collected in the wads, consequently if these are not shaken out the drier part becomes over-dried whilst the wads are becoming dry enough for the rest of the operation to be proceeded with.

The invention of the mowing machine and its general adaptation throughout the country have completely changed the features of haymaking. We give an illustration of a two-horse grass mower, by means of which 10 or 12 acres of grass may be conveniently mown in one day, one man and two horses only being employed. The three chief things to be attended to in using a grass-mower are sharpening, oiling, and driving; the rest will then take care of itself. A good machine is an immense advantage to a farmer, if he has a careful man to drive it, or if he drives it himself; by setting to work at three o'clock in the morning several acres may be cut before the heat of the day comes on, and without oppressing either man or horses. The grass

Two horses had to work hard in the hay loader. Not only had they to pull the growing load, but also provided power for the ground-driven machinery that activated the loader tines.

is down ready for the morning's sun; and both man and horse, after an hour's rest, are at liberty for other work.

Grass that is cut by machine lies in good form for drying, and it may be left so until next day, unless the weather is unusually hot and there is a danger of its being sunburnt. It is difficult to shake out machine swathes by hand or with a fork, when they want tedding, simply because they are so much spread over the land; and to do the work well a tedding-machine, or hay-maker, is required. However valuable a mower may be, a tedder is hardly less so; indeed, the latter will do all that is required in settled weather to make the hay dry enough for stacking, and it is a good plan to keep it going all day, repeatedly stirring the hay about, mixing it well up together, leaving it so light on the ground that sun and wind can get freely into making it better and quicker than can be done by hand. In very hot weather the tedder is particularly valuable; the hay requires to be constantly kept stirring, so that the sun may not scorch a portion of it while the rest is still under-made.

In good weather the hay will not require touching at all by hand. The mower cuts it; the tedders stirs it about, leaving it light on the field; the sun and wind dry it, and it is ready for stacking. At this stage a horse-rake will be found a most useful implement, doing the work of six or eight men, who are thus set at liberty for carting and stacking. A horse-rake with four-feet-six wheels will collect the hay into rows that are quite thick enough to cart from, leaving the ground much cleaner than would be done by hand, and in long hay leaving it so clean that it will require no raking afterwards; in short hay it will generally be found necessary to rake the ground after the "putting-in" is done, but this the horse-rake will do, crossing the direction taken before and raking perfectly clean. A boy riding and a light horse will do a large amount of the work in a very short time with one of these self-acting horse-rakes, and a farmer with 20 acres of hay will always be repaid in a short time the capital laid out in buying one of them.

These three machines - the mower, the tedder, and the raker-costing no more than one middling horse, are an excellent investment for a farmer who cuts 50 to 60 acres of meadow grass; and even on small farms a one-horse mower, with a small tedder and horse-rake, will pay excellent interest on the outlay, enabling the farmer to do more work in less time and with fewer hands than could be done under the old-fashioned system of hay-making.

A hay loader has two wheels, as wide as a waggon, and coupled to the hind axle, and high enough to reach to the top of a load. As the waggon moves along the wind-rows the loader behind gathers the hay up with its revolving web, and deposits it in the waggon. A man on the waggon builds it into its place, and when his load is complete he unhitches the loader and drives to the stack. A man or boy is usually in attendance at the loader to couple it and uncouple it on to the waggon, and to lead the horses along the wind-rows.

The sweep rake consists of a wooden framework 14ft. wide on two wheels, with times or fingers 10ft. long and 18 in. apart fixed to the frame. The horses are yoked one at each side with pole straps to poles parallel to the tines at each side-outside the wheels —and pull from a whippletree attached to short poles level with the axle of the wheels. A triangular frame carried on a swivel wheel is hinged on behind, and carries a seat for the driver, and a screw wheel which depresses the points or tines on to the ground. The horseman drives his sweep rake so that the tines slip under the hay, and scoop it up whether it be in wind-rows, heaps, or cocks. A sweep rake will ordinarily hold two-thirds of a cartload. The poles prevent the hay from going over the sides on to the horses, and the frame at the back prevents it from going over there. The sweep rake when full is driven up to the stack and backed out, leaving the load lying on the ground. The sweep rake is now largely used in northern districts for dragging the cocks or hay in wind-rows up to the centres where the ricking or 'pyking' is being done in the field, and is a great advance on the old system of gathering with two horses hitched to a rope passed round the cocks, or the use of a plank and chains.

The cheapest and simplest form of stacking machinery is the horse fork. It is merely a form of crane, and consists of a long pole erected in the ground carrying a gaff. A rope works over the end of the gaff, with a horse at one end and a large iron grab at the other. The grab is lowered into the load of hay on the waggon, the man on the waggon forcing the points of the grab into the load. The horse working the crane moves forward and raises the grab full of hay up on to the stack. The grab is provided with a patent catch which, when loosened, opens the tines and lets the hay fall out. This catch is operated automatically or by a cord from the ground. Horse forks are not very largely used in conjunction with the sweep rake, as the hay in a sweep load is not in such a compact form as on a waggon where it has been built, consequently the grab cannot get a big load and time is lost.

A rick lifter is a very low cart without sides and drawn by a horse. This is backed against the rick, and the end of it tipped on to the ground against the bottom of the rick. The lifter is provided with a wind-lass, and a rope or chain is put round the base of the rick and wound up, and as it tightens the hay slides on to the platform, which is then brought back to the level and is taken to the stack.

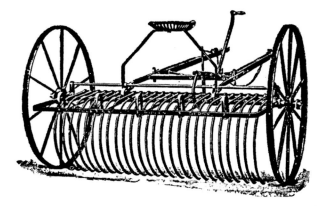
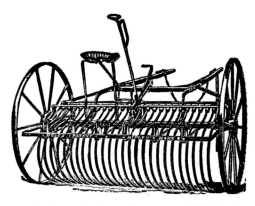

The two types of horse rake are shown here. The self-acting model uses the horse's power to lift the tines by engaging a lever, while in the manual type the horseman pulls a lever each time the tines are full. Tipping is done to ensure straight lines or windrows across the field. Horserakes were sometimes used to row up before cocking or piking, but mainly for 'clean' raking after the hay has been gathered.

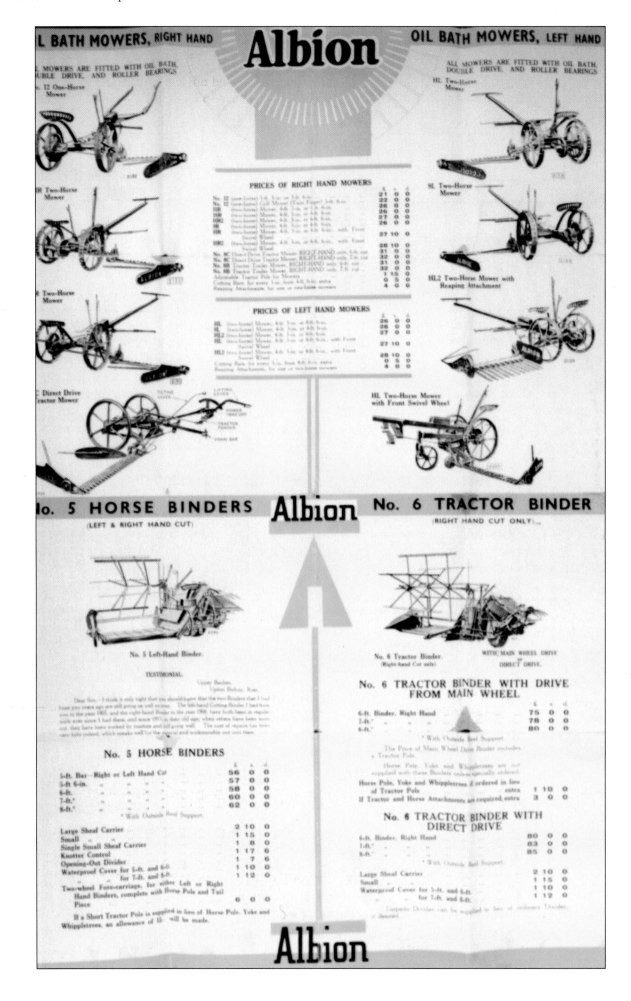

1. *Hornsby's "Paragon" Mower.*

2. *Samuelson's Combined Mower & Reaper.*

3. *Hay Maker.*

Three types of early hay equipment. The mower-reaper (2) was used for corn, which fell onto the slatted platform to be raked off in sheaf sizes.
Opposite: *Inside of an advertising leaflet for Albion reapers and horse rakes.*

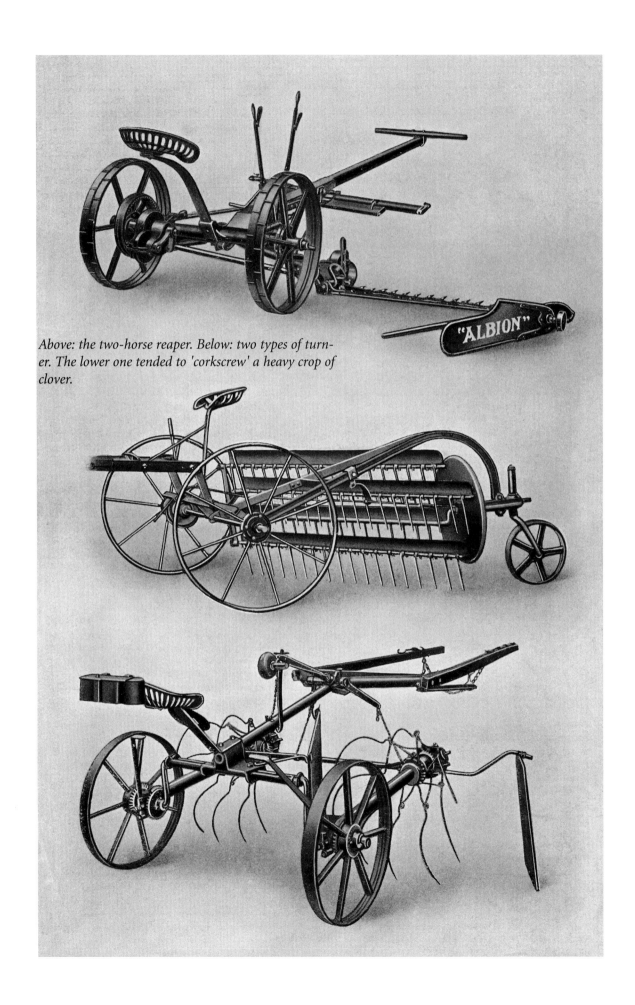

Above: the two-horse reaper. Below: two types of turner. The lower one tended to 'corkscrew' a heavy crop of clover.

Hay loader in operation.

The hay rick lifter is backed against the pike or small stack, and the end of the lifter tipped onto the ground against it. The lifter has a windlass which tightens a chain or rope around the base of the pike, and as it tightens the hay slides onto the platform which is then returned to the level.

Thistle Reaper

Side-Delivery Reaper

Above: *A modern power driven grass cutter fitted to a land driven bogey to enable it to be used with horses. Note: Operator's seat on rear.*

Below: *This thistle cutter is beginning to show signs of decay.*

This plate of spare parts enabled the farmer or his blacksmith to order by number. Such a system relied on the post or telegraph to order them, railways to deliver, and banks to pay for the order. Until these facilities were available, farmers were restricted to local repairs.

STAND No. 146 ROYAL SHOW.

THE "QUICKWORK" SECTION REMOVER
AND RIVETER

A section can be removed and replaced in a few seconds and a knife completely rebladed in a few moments.

LOW IN PRICE

BETTER THAN OTHERS

BRITISH MADE

COMMANDS A READY SALE

GEO. HENDERSON, 18 FORTH ST., EDINBURGH

The riveting gadget advertised in 1934 was a boon in a busy haytime, helping keep reaper blades up to scratch.

Grinding and sharpening machine for reaper knives.

One-horse mower. (The Medici Society Ltd).

Bevel-wheel Knife Grinder

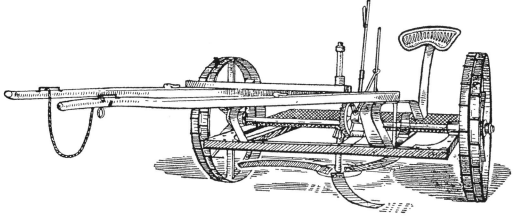

*This thistle cutter was a fore-run-
ner of todays flail mower.*

Right: Patent horse fork and elevator. A horse operated pulley and grab lifted the hay from the cocks on to the large stacks.

A hay rack lifter. The hay cock was pulled on by a hand-operated drum and chain.

A loaded hay rick lifter. This one has a horse-wheel for drawing loads aboard by horse-power rather than by hand.

Two-horse hay sweep. A pair of steady animals was needed, as they worked at a considerable distance from each other.

With the turn-over sweep, below, the driver puts slight weight on the handles while moving the sweepful of hay, then lifts them slightly so the tines stick into the ground, and the whole apparatus turns turtle without stopping the horse. It then rights itself.

Below: Taken by a book customer friend of many years' standing, though we never met. F F McFarlane was 83 when he sent this. 'Nearing the end of the great era', he wrote. 'Like the horses, the man was well shod and tidy'. Scene is near Craigmill, Stirling, with the Wallace Monument in the background.

This postcard is stamped 1907 and is called haymaking. However, the man in the centre appears to be carrying a sheaf of corn.

HAYMAKING.

Above: *A Joe Godderidge painting. Leading Hay with a pair of Suffolks.*

Below: *Bringing in the hay.*

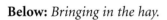

Above: *Valley scene. There must be a long uphill haul to require three horses.*

Above: *The row of pikes and the peaked collar give this a northern feel.*

Harvesting

Side-delivery and sail reapers: evolution to self binder. Root harvest.

Fig. 44.—Cross

A big team hauling a combine harvester on an apparently limitless prairie. The leaders seem a fine pair. Such horses were driven by voice commands, and on them depended the output of the whole team.

A fine harvest in the horse days was one of life's most pleasant experiences. A wet one was purgatory. Most fell in between, but the straining horses, smell of sweat and leather and the clatter and rumble of farm carts and waggons hold memories for those who experienced them.

The self-binder revolutionised harvest. Before its advent, all corn was mown with a scythe or, before that, with a sickle. The corn acreage was limited by the size of the available labour force. Mechanical reapers which laid the corn in long swathes were the first advance, from where the crop still had to be bound into sheaves, using a few strands of the crop itself to do the binding.

Then came the self-delivery or tip reaper, which dropped the cut corn onto a platform, from where it had to be raked off manually into suitably sized sheaves, or slid off to the ground using a lever. In either case, hand tying was still necessary.

The self-binder brought real work for the horses. The standing crop could only be cut after the dew had vanished; otherwise the canvases taking the corn to the knottier became saturated, and tore. This meant working during the hottest part of the day, and the horses had not only to pull the heavy implement, but provide power via the main wheel to work the knife, turn the sails and operate the knotter.

In a dry time with plenty of horse power, it was still very hard work. My grandfather yoked four horses to the binder, and changed two every hour. On a small farm this would not be possible, and old and sometimes lame animals were pressed into service. If the weather was wet, the main or bull wheel would skid along the ground and the machine would block solid. Flies constantly tormented the teams.

The crop had then to be stooked. This entailed smacking a pair of sheaves together and then another and another, until a stook of eight or ten sheaves was formed. If the rains continued, these had to be restooked, to prevent corn sprouting in the ear; former varieties were much more prone to holding water.

The last all-horse harvest in which I took part was during the golden summer of 1949. This 200 acres Vale of York farm had five horses and, incredible as it now seems, a harvest team of seven men and lads. Two – a man and a lad – built the stack. Four lads drove the horses to three single carts

The McCormick reaper of the early 1850s. A similar one was awarded the Gold Medal of Innovation at the Great Exhibition in London, 1851. Irish-American Cyrus Hall McCormick invented this practical harvesting machine. The world's first, it followed an 1831 model, which was improved and developed in ensuing years. Other manufacturers brought out their own versions, establishing a new industry. McCormick founded International Harvester Co., worldwide.

and a pair rulley. The fulcrum of the whole operation was the forker in the field. He was often a middle-aged man who could be relied on to fork sheaves two at a time for hours on end. He was often a former horseman, but now preferred to keep his feet on the ground. He determined the pace of the whole operation, and the boss's continual admonition was 'keep the forker going'.

Thus as soon as an empty cart returned to the field with its neat rows of stooks, the vehicle being loaded would have a rope slung over, and be bid on its way even if little more than half full. The loaded cart would make its swaying way through the narrow gateways and over deceptive, bridged gutters, arriving in the stackyard to bantering comments if its load was other than precisely square. It would draw alongside the stack, and the lad who had loaded it would 'team' each sheaf in precisely the right place to ease the stacker's lot. If done carelessly, the sheaf might be slung back in his face.

'Draw your waggons into a circle!' proclaimed Dick Wood, soaked in Wild West films. We solemnly did so as our line of empty vehicles returned after lunch, spurting back to the field before the Boss saw such frivolities. Despite such interludes, that harvest was completed with no overtime beyond seven o'clock. Then the horses were unharnessed, led to their pasture under a rising moon and released by swinging their heads towards the gate so that their flicking heels flashed harmlessly in the soft summer air.

Root harvest was less glamourous but equally

Burgess & Key's reaper. 'Safety First' was not a consideration where working men were concerned at that time, witness the precarious driving seat.

vital. Sugar beets were lifted and topped by hand, the roots being loosened first by means of a lifting plough with deep-set share. Sometimes the tops were piled into small heaps, in which state they would remain fresh for many days. Mechanical toppers were on trial, but seldom reached the necessary accuracy, and had to be followed by hand trimming.

'Harvest to Christmas' was the busiest time of the year on a typical mixed farm. Potatoes were lifted by spinning them out from the row, a suspended sack halting the more jet-propelled tubers and depositing them in a workable line. Then the gangs, mainly of women and children, gathered them into buckets, which they tipped over the cart sides.

Rubber wheeled carts had lower axles, and consequently lower sides, making tipping easier. They had disadvantages in a wet time for, instead of following the ruts as the iron-tyred carts did, these modern inventions were liable to 'sholl', or slide at an angle instead of running true.

The work was hard on the horses, battling with mud. They did, however, receive some rest when tipping the load, and when waiting for buckets to be emptied into their carts. Horses had the great advantage of remote control. A word, usually followed by their name, sufficed to send them forward to the next stopping point. Jumping on and off a noisy, fume-laden tractor was never as pleasant.

In the 1880s, this single-horse binder followed behind the reaper, binding sheaves separately. Such tentative steps in mechanical progress tend to be forgotten, but show how our ancestors experimented and tried different methods until they arrived at the self-binder model destined to be manufactured with little change for over half a century.

Three horses drawing a binder at Church Farm, Swainby, North Yorkshire. Note the postilion rider on the offside horse, and the couplings bit to bit.

A self-binding reaper harvesting oats. The presence of dogs is not recommended; horrible accidents have occurred.

Side-on view of binder cutting corn in the Darlington area.

Rear view of three-horse binder at Hollybush Farm, Newsham, Barnard Castle.

Clear working side view of a binder at Prospect Farm, Greatham, Co. Durham.

Four binders, each with four horses, and five men with various types of scythe, plus four with sheaf-gathering rakes. The scythesmen are either 'opening out' the field, mowing a path for the binder, or more probably cutting difficult laid areas.

A three-horse team, binder, and gang stooking close up to the binder. When I was horseman for Harry Rockliff at Askham Bryan, York, he used to talk of his days on a larger farm when he simply daren't break down with the binder, as there was always a man waiting ready to pick up the last sheaf.

Changing the spool of binder twine. On many farms binder twine was known as 'Massey Harris' through its associations with the binder makers.

Three men manhandling a binder. The big disadvantage of horse yokes for a binder was the lack of any effective means of backing.

Binder and various other machines at Beamish Home Farm.

Arthur Lea on the trace horse, Castleside area, Co. Durham.

Three good strong horses of the type needed for this very heavy work. It can only be done when the dew has risen, otherwise the binder canvasses become damp, taut and then tear. Bindering also co-incides with the height of the fly season, adding to the horses' discomfort.

Three horses and unstooked sheaves in the foreground. There was a knack in stooking; taking a sheaf under each arm the stooker smacked the butts into the stubble, at the same time bringing the heads smartly together so that they intermingled. One night during World War II, two Home Guards were on watch against a German invasion on a plateau, part of which was a field of unstooked corn, and as it was a bright moonlight night they stooked the farmer's field to pass the time.

Binder rider on the middle horse as storm clouds gather. School boys often undertook this task, which coincided with summer holidays. A boy's weight was little extra burden, but the horse's sweat soon caused our legs to chafe, for short trousers were then the rule.

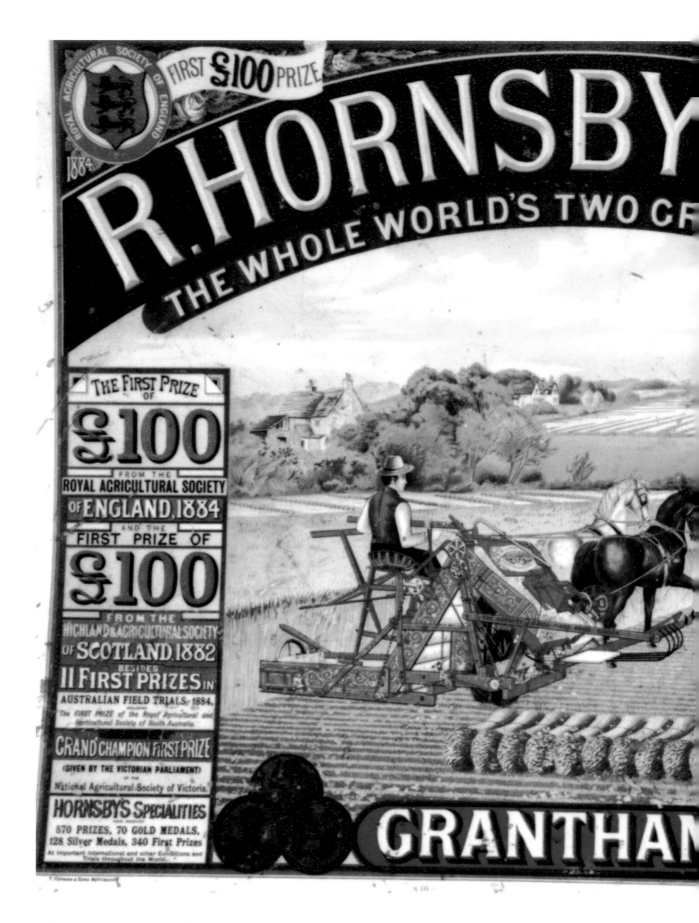

Advertisement for Hornsby's Royal First Prize Binder.

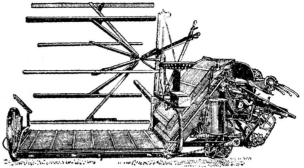

Fig. 1.—Rear View of Binder (J. Wallace & Sons, Ltd.)

Rear view of another well known make - Wallace.

Rear view of Massey Harris binder, with the mysteries of the knotter revealed (below).

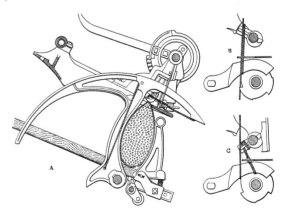

The first power-driven binder in Caithness. Scene is Ackergill Mains, Wick, 1917. There is a strong heavy horse tradition in northern Scotland, and it was a stronghold of The Horseman's Word and other magical rites. See pages 132-3.

A large gang to tie up sheaves in a rather tangled crop of oats. A sail reaper at Auchnagatt, Aberdeenshire, in 1913.

A pair of black Percherons in USA. The crop appears light and the going firm, otherwise the work would be beyond the capacity of a pair over a prolonged period.

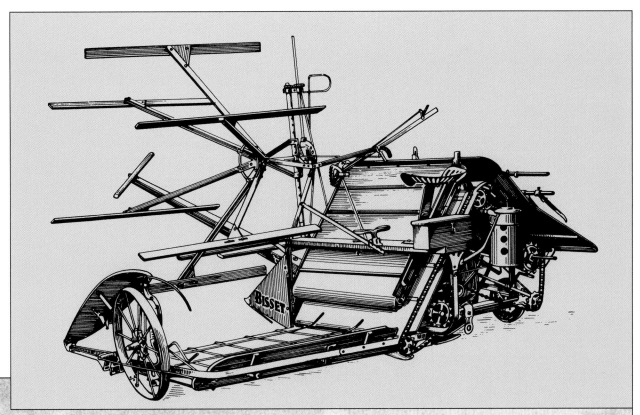

Steel frame binder by John Bisset and Sons Ltd. Blairgowie.

Stables and

Barn

Machinery

Fig. 44.—Cross

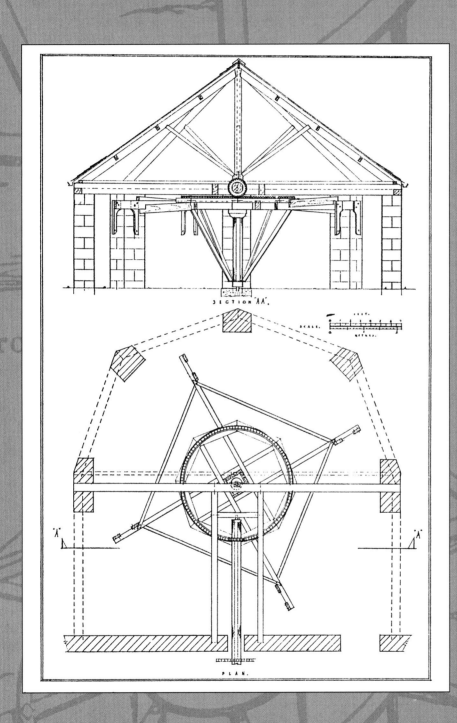

Some aspects of horse-drawn husbandry are natural artists' subjects, taking the eye instantaneously. Among them is a plough team coming over the brow of a hill, a binder majestically moving round a standing field of oats in bright sunshine, or a timber waggon among autumn leaves, six horses straining.

Barn machinery is less glamourous. Barn machinery is a generic term for a whole range of items which work on a day-by-day basis, preparing feed for stock. Root pulpers, cake crushers, oat rollers and even threshers come into this category.

Power generated by the horse's forward walk has to be transformed into circular motion. The simplest way of so doing was to fix a toothed iron wheel horizontally into the ground, and fix on a wooden shaft to which the horse was attached. By walking round and round, the horse conveyed power through a gearing mechanism to drive from one to four small machines.

The first oil cakes imported as cattle food arrived at the end of the eighteenth century. They were in inch-thick oblong blocks, too hard to be eaten whole. Machines were devised with toothed rollers to break up the cakes, thereby making them easier on the animals' teeth.

Overhead horse gear was first used in England and Scotland in the eighteenth and early nineteenth centuries. It was massive, requiring a large barn and a capital investment beyond the reach of all but the larger farmers and landowners. A toothed wooden crown wheel was secured horizontally on a vertical post, well above head height, and up to 16 feet in diameter. Angled wooden cross-pieces were affixed to the crown wheel above and to the horse's swingletree below. Two horses were used, going round and round. A drive shaft and pinion transmitted power to the thresher, cake breaker or mill.

The skilled wheelwrights of those days built such wheels to last, but they fell into disuse when smaller stationary engines arrived on the farming scheme.

After the turn of the nineteenth century, ground horse gear became available. The wheel was rotated by horse power in the same way, but the large crown wheel was replaced by a toothed drive wheel some three feet in diameter. It was secured to a strong timber frame flat on the ground, and the horses had to step over the drive shaft leading to the machinery. This was unsatisfactory and the cause of accidents, but the horses could take a larger and more comfortable circle. A wooden bridge or ramp was sometimes installed to protect the horses' legs, but this entailed an uphill followed by a downhill track. These cheaper horse wheels were within the compass of medium-sized farms, witness the 'wheelhouse' of circular, hexagonal or octagonal design which became such a farm feature. Sadly, many of these picturesque buildings were destroyed when the horse was substituted by the undoubtedly more handy stationary engine, and only recently has there been much effort to save them. They tended to disappear altogether, as their design did not lend itself to alternative use.

By the mid-nineteenth century, designs of gears and shafts improved. Barrett, Exall and Andrews of Reading brought out a safe, neat and efficient gear, with an 18-inches diameter vertical cast-iron drum standing only 24 inches high. As with earlier gears, the horses were yoked to radial poles, and their circular movement was received onto a vertical shaft. Through gearing, each revolution of the horses was stepped up to 33 revolutions on the drive shaft. A universal coupling joint on the drive shaft enabled the gear to be dismantled, and reconnected to another machine.

By 1860, horse gears had achieved high mechanical efficiency. But they were to be usurped by the small stationary or portable steam engines.

In North America, the treadmill principle functioned far more widely than in Britain. The unfortunate horses had to try to keep their feet by endlessly paddling on a wide upward-sloping belt geared to threshing or timber milling operations.

Root pulpers powered by wheel horses became a necessary item of equipment, particularly on large arable and mixed farms where fertility was maintained by feeding the roots to a foldyard of fattening bullocks. The bigger machines could deal with five tons of roots an hour, which seems a lot for a daily operation, but the skilled feeders of those days seldom weighed their rations. When the big beasts started to lie down to chew the cud, the feeder was satisfied. 'Give 'em another scuttleful and mak' 'em lie down!' was a common injunction.

A development of the barn-based root cutter was the turnip-slicing cart. After topping and tailing, the roots were forked into a cart which had a cutting wheel affixed inside at the rear.

It was driven by gearing from the cart's wheels as the horse moved forward. The sliced roots dropped through an aperture onto the ground in a steady stream, which enabled a large flock of sheep to be fed without too much pushing and boring.

The cutting wheel could be put in and out of gear. It turned at a good speed, taking the roots which rolled onto its knives via the cart's sloping false floor. This floor could be removed when the cart was needed for another job.

The cider mill was very important in traditional cider-making areas, mainly in the south-west and the south-east. A stone or concrete trough, circular in shape, was filled evenly with the crop, which was crushed by a great stone roller bevelled to follow the track of the trough. A strong pony often sufficed for power, and the juice was crushed out and gathered for use. Incidentally, horse hair was used to make mattresses which filtered the pulp, and Suffolk horse breeders tell me that bags hung in every stable to take any hair removed during grooming and mane combing. This was sold to cider making counties like Herefordshire and Shropshire, and made a nice bonus for the horsemen.

GIN GANS

A 'gin-gan' is Northumbrian for 'horse wheel', and that county housed many well-constructed examples. The large farms of the area invariably wintered many beef cattle with large appetites for the chopped turnips which formed much of their rations, and Scottish arable farms had similar examples. When a Scottish cattleman was told that turnips were 'mainly watter', he instantly replied 'It must be by-ordinary watter'.

The inside of this gin-gan was rebuilt at Beamish Home Farm, and it and many more interesting items are still on view. Most of the structure came from Berwick Hills Low Farm.

The wooden structure in this building was turned by four horses, each harnessed into one of the wooden "yokes". A circular rack gear on top of it turned a wooden shaft which ran through into the barn behind to drive a threshing machine.

"Gin Gans", their Northumbrian dialect name, were mostly built between about 1800 and 1850, after the invention of a successful threshing machine

by Andrew Meikle in 1788. Although this structure was originally built here, the wooden horsewheel was taken out many years ago and the machine shown here came from Berwick Hill Farm near Ponteland. The thresher came from Woodhouse Farm, Belsay.

A gin-gan at West Farm, Framlington, Northumberland. There is an unusual number of pillars in the structure, one of which is cylindrical.

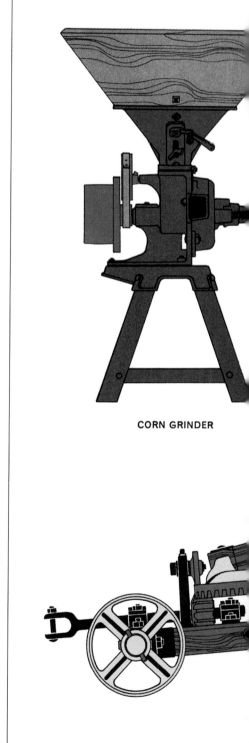

CORN GRINDER

Horse gear (below) and some of the machines it drove. The Perkins horse gear was made around 1840 at Hitchin, Hertfordshire. It was 64 inches long, 58 inches wide, with a height of 23 inches and a 9 ft 3 in pole. It weighed between 5 and 6 cwt. The corn grinder was built by Bentall at Heybridge in 1920, while the hand-operated oil cake breaker was made by Corbett & Peele at Shrewsbury in 1895. It changed hands for £1 in 1970. The Wrekin root pulper dates from 1920.

ROOT PULPER

OIL CAKE BREAKER

HORSE GEAR

Carts and

Waggons

County by County

Fig. 44.—Cross

A Hampshire waggon owned by Mr Joy of Bentley. John Thompson in Carts, Carriages and Caravans, 1980, asks: 'Where has this party been?' They look pleased with their mode of transport.

A market cart. A maid-of-all-work that transported calves or any small livestock as well as the family and their groceries.

A splendid row of old faithfuls at John Harris's Epworth farmyard.

Below: *A tipping cart in all its detail. It shows the stilts or leaners by which the shafts were propped up when the horse was 'loosed out'. The wheels had to be chocked to prevent the cart slewing and thereby pushing over the stilts. This was particularly important when a heavy load was left in. The order of unyoking was 1, breechings chains; 2, backband; 3, shoulder chains. This was to minimise damage if the horse walked forward. It was important for the load to be reasonably balanced, or the men could not support the weight of the shafts or, if light on, (too much weight behind) they would go up in the air. It was essential to see that no chains were catching when the horse was led forward. This cart was built in 1925 by Langley of Frampton. Its previous owners were Measures and Sanderson of Wainfleet.*

This Wolds waggon's beautiful lines were built at Lebberston. Mr Hill of Hunmanby on the Yorkshire coast was the previous owner.

In the centre is a heavy pole waggon with fittings to take an extra pair of horses in front. Rims are wide, and were preferred by road maintainers as they cut in less. Owner John Harris, dated 1924.

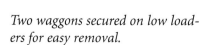

Two waggons secured on low loaders for easy removal.

The artistry in this iron-tyred farm cart rivals that of caravan or narrow boat owners. This scene at a farm sale looks intrinsically right.

The Walkington Hayride, Beverley, East Yorkshire, re-enacted the times when a day trip to the sea-side was a highlight of childhod summers. Waggons were cleaned, and the teams groomed and decorated to take the village children to the nearest railway station. This waggon was built by Cooke of Lincoln in 1898.

A Cotswold waggon built by Stokes of Broadway in 1895. Marshall in his Rural Economy of Gloucestershire noted that it was ' beyond all argument the best farm waggon I have seen in the Kingdom'

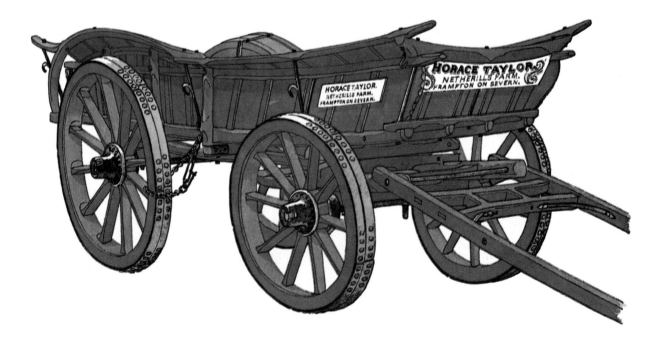

Cart shed at High Flatts Farm, Chester-le-Street, Co Durham. Traditional cart sheds are among the most cherished of the older farm buildings. They were open-fronted, and the brick or stone pillars often bear scars of scrapes from iron-tyred carts being backed into them.

Farm cart, showing pins removed for tipping.

Rubber tyred farm carts were deemed an improvement, being quieter on roads and with supposedly less draught. However, when carting root crops in a wet autumn, the rubber tyred cart was liable to 'sholl' or move sideways as well as forwards, and not all farm workers approved of the change.

Under view of an unprovenanced coup cart after some restoration. Note the side boards.

Long cart. A spindle-sided harvest cart from Mr. Storrow, Willimontswick Castle Farm. In use until 1964.

Detail of harvest cart, J Blair, Lane End.

Back of the cart. Mount Pleasant, Crookham. The maker's name is Wm Elder & Sons Ltd, Berwick-on-Tweed. The Tweed Valley was and is a noted arable area, and record crops of grain have been grown there. It also had substantial flocks of arable sheep, based on the Scottish Halfbred, that added much to the soil's fertility .

Here's a cart with a difference. A dandy cart at Throckley Colliery, Northumberland. The early railways era, when the horse rode down the incline in the cart, having pulled it up.

Newly painted cart standing in front of a cartwright's and painter's shop. These crafts were closely linked. The young lad on the left named Haughton went on to become an outstanding cart painter.

Above: *Cattle cart or bull float. Most were owned by dealers or pedigree cattle exhibitors. Such solid-sided low-loaders helped keep stock quiet in transit.*

Wholesale milk was taken to the nearest railway station in a light cart. There was invariably a race to beat the train. One milk pony near Sheriff Hutton, York, delivered to Flaxton station, and when the approaching engine blew its whistle the pony changed from a smart trot to a gallop!

Sally Gray's bullock cart; a popular feature at local Welsh shows.

A light double-shafted waggon with heather in bloom in the background. Are the ladies picking bilberries?

Hermaphrodite waggon. The fore part was added to convert a cart into a waggon for harvest. This model was built by Cooke of Lincoln in 1904, and was bought by John Harris from B A Neave, Grayingham, Lincolnshire.

Well-maintained horse-drawn fire engine, property of Key Bros., Folkingham, Lincolnshire.

Cart with racks or gaumers to facilitate loading such bulk as loose hay or sheaves of corn.

A Glamorgan waggon, drawn by Donald J Smith. Note the curves over the rear wheels.

An 0xfordshire waggon (Donald J Smith).

Yorkshire farm waggon at Beck Isle Museum, Pickering, North Yorkshire. Well worth a visit for lots of farming material.

CHAPTER 9

Harness,

Attachments

and

Decorations

Swingletrees, balks, chains, and wood blocks

"STEADY THERE."

A genuine working horse, with neat pony-like ears. This 1925 card depicts a leather head collar with detachable bit.

The horse brasses played an incalculable part in raising the morale of several generations of horsemen. These treasured brasses were invariably owned by the employed horseman. His employer might possess a set, but only if he himself was an enthusiast, and enjoyed ploughing matches or feasts and processions.

There has been much debate about the origins of horse brasses, claimed by some to have been used to ward off the evil eye. Though many horsemen were undoubtedly superstitious, I have never known any who regarded brasses as other than pure decoration.

The horse brass collection of the working horseman was the equivalent of crook making to the hill shepherd. Both lived in primitive and sometimes lonely accommodation. Both were devoted to their profession; the shepherd seldom talked of anything except his sheep and associated activities; the horseman's life revolved around his charges.

Let us step back into those early cottages. Neither gas nor electricity lit them; the glow from a paraffin lamp barely sufficed for reading. Under the dull light and from the fire's flickering flames was sufficient light to whittle a stick or clean and examine a brass. Television had not been invented and even a wireless or radio was a rarity in working people's homes before World War Two.

When the team was going on a public road the next day, an extra effort would be made to assemble and polish the brasses. If a four-horse waggon was setting out to the mill or railway station, probably before daybreak, each brass would be assessed to a particular horse. Blossom and Bonny at the wheel, might wear face brasses reflecting the sun's rays, while Beauty and Blackbird in the lead might sport a sheaf of corn or an acorn.

Some horsemen would have bells, or a bell contained in a brass. All had to be polished, and even this was an item when wages were around £1 per week in the early 1900's, and only 32 shillings (£1.60) per week in the early 1930's.

Though most farmers were also very hard up, some bought polish for the brasses and blacking for the harness.

In 'Amongst Farm Horses' by Stephen Caunce , there is an account of an East Riding of Yorkshire farmer, Mr Hornby of Kilham, who would buy polish, dubbin and ribbons for his horselads.

"I mean, if you were just working in the fields would you leave it or -?

Mr T: Why, clean t'brasses, like – you would keep your brasses clean.

Mr P: You only used to bother just wi' collar – and some didn't even have backband traces, did they. Some just had loose traces."

Their time was not the only thing the lads gave in search of a good turnout: on nearly all farms they also paid for their own brasses, cleaners, and harness decorations. Mr Rispin bought his from the Kilham saddler:

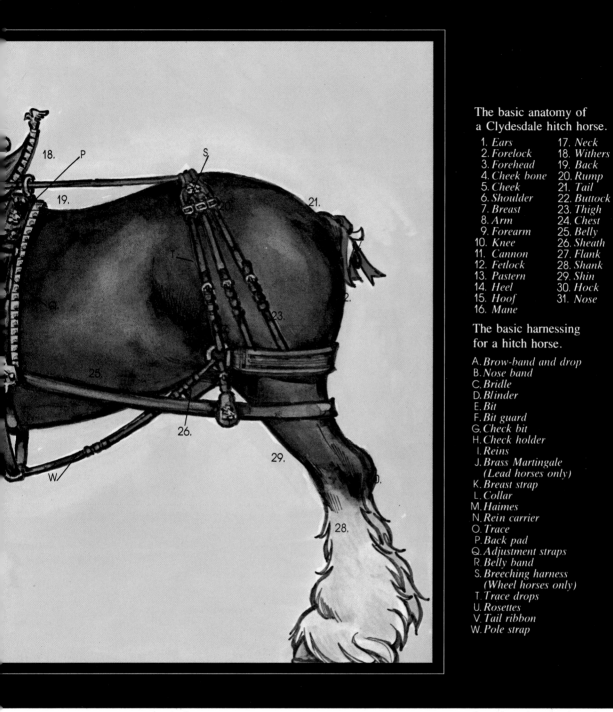

The basic anatomy of
a Clydesdale hitch horse.

1. *Ears*	17. *Neck*
2. *Forelock*	18. *Withers*
3. *Forehead*	19. *Back*
4. *Cheek bone*	20. *Rump*
5. *Cheek*	21. *Tail*
6. *Shoulder*	22. *Buttock*
7. *Breast*	23. *Thigh*
8. *Arm*	24. *Chest*
9. *Forearm*	25. *Belly*
10. *Knee*	26. *Sheath*
11. *Cannon*	27. *Flank*
12. *Fetlock*	28. *Shank*
13. *Pastern*	29. *Shin*
14. *Heel*	30. *Hock*
15. *Hoof*	31. *Nose*
16. *Mane*	

The basic harnessing
for a hitch horse.

A. *Brow-band and drop*
B. *Nose band*
C. *Bridle*
D. *Blinder*
E. *Bit*
F. *Bit guard*
G. *Check bit*
H. *Check holder*
I. *Reins*
J. *Brass Martingale*
   (Lead horses only)
K. *Breast strap*
L. *Collar*
M. *Haimes*
N. *Rein carrier*
O. *Trace*
P. *Back pad*
Q. *Adjustment straps*
R. *Belly band*
S. *Breeching harness*
   (Wheel horses only)
T. *Trace drops*
U. *Rosettes*
V. *Tail ribbon*
W. *Pole strap*

17

Though a show rather than a working harness, this Anheuser-Busch Clydesdale picture outlines both the parts of the horse's body and pole harness. The type of bit on a working horse would be different, and there would be no brass martingale, but it is a very good diagram.

The way they were. Many years elapsed before horses took over from oxen in British fields, and even now there is renewed interest in them. I had a student who had worked ox teams in Australia, and said that they would haul timber up steep, rough banks that no horse would look at.

"He had bells and all, he had some, you know, as used to have bells on. . . .

I suppose they must have spent a bit of money on their horses, really?

Oh aye, aye. Aye, they did. . . . This Hornby, when he farmed [in Kilham], he always used to buy polish to polish the gearing, like – why dubbin and all such as that, and he would buy 'em their ribbons. You know, they'd wear all sorts o' different colours o' ribbons, tie – when you tied their tails up – he was very good for that. . . . But I've never lived at a spot where they did that.

But you used to buy them yourselves, anyway?

Yes. Oh aye, used to buy 'em yourself."

Each lad had his own set of harness which he guarded jealously. Interference with another lad's was considered a deadly crime, and even more sacrosanct was the special set of gears reserved for use with the best waggon on special trips. The waggoner looked after it as well as his own set, and woe betide any lad who borrowed any part of it

without express instructions, which would only be forthcoming if the waggoner could not be spared from the job he was on and a substitute had to take the waggon out. When a waggon made a trip off the farm, the farmer's name and address were clearly displayed on the side, and he expected it to look its best, but during normal work most farmers left the horses' appearance entirely to the lads. Mr Fisher remarked, 'No, as long as they were getting t'work done and that, they never bothered much.'

They only became personally interested when their horses were on display to the public, especially at shows or other village festivals, booning days when a new farmer was given a free day's labour by all his neighbours, or similar occasions. Then the good name of the farm was at stake and lavish decoration was looked for. Yet the lads still got no time off to make their preparations, the farmers relying instead on their concern for their own prestige to make them willing to sit up half the night getting everything ready. Mr Rispin related how he took

Going Home, by Jane M Parkin. Plough harness, seat of the driver and the horse's tiredness are well depicted.

Complete relaxation epitomised by this pair harnessed to a pole, probably pulling a light waggon. Open bridles, and leather reins coiled round the hames. The card is from Belgium.

This active-looking pair are more like vanners or 'half-legged' horses rather than true heavies. Harnessed to a pole in the harvest field, they wear small winkers or blinkers. The postcard bears a King George V halfpenny stamp.

some Kilham children to the seaside as part of a cavalcade of waggons from every farm in the village:

'Oh [they were] decorated up, you know – it was a big occasion was that. Flowers on t'britch-bands and all that there, and bows and all.... I took 'em one Wednesday, when I come back at night time – well, you set off at six and then it was nine o'clock when you got back at night – used to be a three-hour going to Brid, you know, with a waggon. And when I come back at night, foreman said, 'You haven't to take nowt off that gearing!' I had to go to Driffield next day, just two in t'wag-gon; he always liked horses and I had to go right the way along t'back street and then right away up t'front street just to show the horses. Aye. And I believe I only wanted a barrel o'beer back with me. That was all I wanted. But it was just to show them off. Aye. But he was like that.

On normal jobs there was often little harness to be decorated and, in any case, you didn't want a lot because it was making it heavy for them, you see. Oh, you used to plait their tails, and a bit o'ribbon and a brass or two at front," said Mr Fisher. Many lads simply concentrated on keeping everything neat and clean, especially boys who had insufficient money to begin buying decorations. The intricate plaiting of the tail with interwoven ribbons of different colours, known as a Scotch bob, was often the only decoration on, for instance, a horse that was ploughing. Even where the routine made it difficult, however, lads would do their best to turn out a good looking team. Mr Tate said:

'I could always tie a horse tail as well as anybody, it didn't matter a bugger who he was, I could tie a tail up on him. I've tied 'em up hundreds of times walking behind them, walking to t'field. We never had time at Wilde's farm to tie 'em up before you went to work.'

Modern Farm Open Days and 'Work-ins' seek to emulate the scenes. This is how the Southern Counties Heavy Horse Association writer Lee Weatherley described it in their Heavy Horse Handbook a 'Spring Working of Heavy Farm Horses' on a Hampshire Farm.

'Nick Rayner, owner of the farm, has eight horses of his own. All the work was real, not just for show; the work his own horses would normally do. On that occasion the horses wore only their working harness. But a tradition of the horse ploughing matches, also revived, is the Best Turn-Out, which

Trace harness on the Liverpool docks. Raw cotton came by ship from India, and thence by rail to the Lancashire cotton mills. These horses provided the link between docks and railhead. Liverpool had its own style of harness.

means, as one old ploughman put it: 'Polishin' the whole 'orse'. Over the gleaming coat goes the complete parade harness, the bright horse brasses shining against the dark leather. The tails and manes are cunningly plaited (there are still specialists in this art) and decorative ear-muffs are put on'.

If you arrive early enough to see all this being prepared, you can see, and hear, evidence of the pride and affection the horsemen have for their fine animals. One old farmer in Northampton who finally had to have his 24-year old cart mare put down, had her front shoes plated in 24 carat gold. This is a rare tribute, but fortunately another kind is becoming much more common, that of letting the older horses live out their lives in honourable retirement. Harry Reffold in Pie for Breakfast (Halton Press 1984) recalled the pleasure of watching teams decked out for public display.

'But back to "once upon a time," I had ridden my bike to North Cave to a ploughing match. The pairs of horses were arriving yoked to wagons bringing their ploughs, which were unloaded and taken up to their numbered pegs on the headland. Meantime the horses had their final grooming and their manes and tails were plaited up. There were two which took longer to do with the hair parted and twisted into two separate rows. The brass bells would be fastened on top of the headband, the face brasses and martingales. After a final polish, the horse would be ready to be yoked to the plough.

Sometimes the pair of horses would be judged for the smartest turnout, sometimes not, but whatever the conditions the ploughman never took a pair of young horses. It was always his own pair, probably a pair that he had worked for years.

The horses were put to the plough, with traces that had been polished until they shone by putting them into a bag of wheat straw tied by each corner to the wheel of a wagon. Each turn of the wheel sent the chains turning and twisting all the way to the station or mill. One journey worked wonders with a set of traces.

The backbands were on, the traces fastened, the cobbletree and swingletrees were checked, the traces hooked on, and now the plough was set up to the correct width and depth of furrow. Is it nine inches wide and four deep, or is it eight wide and five deep? The stewards will tell him.

The ploughman has been told the number he has drawn when he arrived. Each competitor draws his starting point so he has had time to check what

the land is like, but there is no walking across on his piece to plough. He views it from the end only. There are no bookies shouting the odds, just a few quiet bets amongst the onlookers between themselves, because each man will be fancied.

The depth and width were set, the coulter clean and sharp, the slade clean and shiny, a good sock – one that has had a day's use, just to take the rough edges off it and make it shine. There must be no risk of any soil sticking to any part; it can leave a nasty scar on the face of the turned-up furrow and lose him points.

Herbert Day, who wrote four excellent books on his experiences with farm horses, described how teams were decked out for a new tenant's 'ploughing day'. Before the tractor's advent it was impossible for the new occupier to catch up with land work using only his own horse mower, and neighbours and others sent their ploughs and ploughmen.

On the Brompton Estate, rents were due on Lady Day (25th March), on 5th November, and also on the day when farms changed hands. It was the custom for farmers to give a new tenant a ploughing day. He (Herbert's boss, Bob Pennock) toured the Estate to inform them of the day which had been arranged.

"In March, Bob allowed Ted and myself to take part in a ploughing day. I rarely attached brasses to the harness – unnecessary weight for horses to carry – except on a special occasion such as this. Then the full regalia was on view, including face-pieces, martingales, swingers, bells with red, white and blue brushes attached.

Travelling distances were taken into consideration, but each ploughman worked at least five hours. The only stoppage was at "looance tarm", when a supply of food and a choice of tea or beer was brought to the field.

Old friends met, and the good and bad points of the horses were discussed. It was not unusual to hear the remark: "Ah didn't knaw thoo lived roond eea".

On this particular occasion there were about thirty pairs of horses at work. Brasses gleamed and glittered in the Spring sunshine – an impressive scene unlikely to be witnessed again."

Taking goods to the station was another occasion for dressing the horses in their 'Sunday best'.

Farm wagons drawn by four horses travelling on Wold roads to and from the different stations were

A simplistic view of horse, cart and harness. Model making is a growing hobby. The German Shire modelling society has over one hundred members.

a common sight. On the widest roads there was enough room for two wagons to pass. When this was not possible, an empty wagon was pulled onto the grass verge. If both wagons were loaded, then the nearside wheels on each one turned on the grass verge.

I looked upon "gannin out wi wagon" as a special occasion, a welcome change from walking on the land, and I was informed the day before. In the evening after the stable work was finished I polished my brasses. The next morning, after I had harnessed the horses, I plaited their tails with ribbons.

When the station was situated in a market town, heads were turned to admire the approaching horses. They raised their heads and pricked up their ears. Walking on a hard road between rows of buildings was a different experience from pulling his implements on soft ground in an open field.

It was not unusual on arrival at the station to find the goods yard practically full of wagons and horses. On such occasions I have had problems finding a place to tether my lead horse until I had teamed my wagon.

The return journey to the farm was always pleasurable. You could sense the attitude of the horses when their heads were set for home. Nevertheless, before I left the town my team of horses always stopped of their own accord at a lit-

tle pub called "The Cross Keys". It had been the practice of waggoners in previous years to stop there, and the horses continued the custom."

When holidays were rare, show days were naturally greatly appreciated, as Frederick W Short captured the mood of an unexpected one in 'The Ploughman'.

Ritch, Jane and Semple, all were there. They worked quickly. An air of excitement gripped the byre. Ritch whistled, Jane laughed, Mike forgot his chest and laughed too. Philip joked, whistled and laughed besides. All saw the day with pleasure, even though the others did not think to go to the show. They thought they had no time to leave but they rejoiced in Philip for he was a good one and they wished him well. The whole farm shared in the mood. Even the cows were generous and the milk flowed well – as fluid as the thoughts of a ploughman greeting a victory morn.

Master strode in. He laughed and chucked Jane playfully under the chin. Then he surprised them all, left them dumbfounded with pleasure.

"The whole lot of you can go to the show this afternoon if you get your work done smartly. Of course you'll have to come back for the chores."

Ritch looked at Jane and smiled. Jane smiled back, and then she smiled at the master. Ritch felt a twinge but shook himself in shame. Why should she

Panniers in Devon. Horses carried panniers of basically similar design, and there was a Devon breed of pack horse with long body, now sadly extinct. I have known farmers in the dales who would shovel the bottom furrow at the foot of a slope onto panniers, and take the soil back to the top. Hard work indeed. Those who would abandon British agriculture should remember such efforts.

not smile at the master when he had let them all go to the fair?

Semple grinned in pleasure.

"Can we then take the Missus and the children?" emboldened to ask was he.

"Aye, that you can Mike," said the master, his smile still on the face of the girl.

"By the way Philip here's something for you."

Master fished in his pocket and brought out a brass. It flashed in the light of the candle and took on the shape of a horse shoe. He put his hand in another pocket and drew out a second horse shoe, then a third. He gave them to Philip, smiled and walked out of the door.

They were aghast. Master must have gone daft. Jane thought of the smile and wondered. Ritch thought of that smile and wondered too. Semple had noted the gay of the master and scarcely could believe his eyes. Philip leaned over with pleasure and picked up the weight of his prize.

They all crowded round about him, close to his arm as he stood.

"What is it Philip?" they asked. "It looks like something quite good."

"By golly it's a bit of brass for me harness," he shouted with glee.

"That'll surely look posh on me horses, to-day by golly, by gee."

They laughed, they smiled and admired. Philip ran away with his prize. Right to the stable he went, looking, as if he scarcely could believe his own eyes. He put the pieces up to Jack, to Darling and to Dock too. He stood back and gloated with pleasure, with happiness, good humour too. He chortled and sang and whistled. The fair was his to-day. By tomorrow all the townsfolk would know that he'd really been their way.

Philip seized the straps of the harness, covered them with oil and rubbed well. He polished the rings and the buckles and gave all neat oil. He placed them on the horses, admiring each in turn. Then he took them off again smartly to clean each horse with a brush. Then he oiled the plough and mouldboard and scrubbed the handles as well'.

Eleanor Porter and Mary Abbot described pride in work and appearance farther south in Yeomen of the Cotswolds:

Then there were the days when the teams went 'on the road' delivering the much grain

Above: *Chromographed in Bavaria, this docile looking pair wear open bridles and the pointed collar appears to have strong wooden hames.*

then grown; and for this there would be much bur-nishing of brasses etc. on harness. Indeed the Carter often had sets of harness specially for these occasions, and many ornaments were added. The 'martingales', a row of shining brasses attached to a broad band of leather that passed between the horse' fore legs, bells on the mullens, ribbons and so forth, all making a brave show of which the horses seemed as proud as their Carter and, be it confessed, often-times the master himself.

Railway facilities were becoming available about this time and the stations within a few miles of most farms, but a fair proportion – especially of wheat – was hauled to the local mills, and in some cases a long journey was involved there.

The roads too were very different, being made of the local limestone. They were soft and cut up badly in winter, hence hauling was a hard job and not infrequently the team would be a four-horse one: forrust, next-to-the-forrust, body and thiller. But to turn out three three-horse teams fit for the road taxed the resources of a twelve-horse stable as there were always some only fit for the land work: too old, too young, a bit lame and so forth.

On road journeys, the Carter carried a long smart whip (kept hung in his cottage) with shining brass bands round the handle. It was seldom used on the horses. A 'bolton' of straw was carried on each load of corn to be bartered for 'a drop of summat' at the favourite pub. This was commuted, though, in some cases for a shilling a load, as the size of the bolton led to bickerings, never large enough etc., and I daresay sometimes the man who tied it and who may, as a boy, have been thrashed by the old carter, had his own back with the straw – in quantity I mean . . .

Even longer journeys were made in taking loads of Cotswolds ram lambs to the fairs on the Berkshire and Wiltshire downs and from these both men and horses would return very tired.

The waggons were often painted a bright yellow with the farmer's name and address, and the date of the last painting inscribed boldly on the front. A man who cared for his implements would have one waggon painted each year. So that, with five or six of such vehicles, all were thus kept in a reasonable state of repair.

Genuine working harness. The hame hook appears blacksmith-made, and the hames are joined by stout leather thongs.

Strong leather head collar, showing ring and clip attached to a rope shank. Tiny, a member of the black Shire team at Thwaites' Star Brewery, Blackburn, Lancashire, meets Mighty the kitten.

Below: *Older readers will remember Charlie Cooke, stud groom to Mr G E Sneath, breeder of the outstanding Percheron stallion Pinchbeck, Union Crest. Men and horse were among the best of the post-World War Two period. This young grey Pinchbeck Union 2nd is a son of the famous sire. He displays the roller used in stallion harness to prevent the horse swinging his head sideways and knocking his handler.*

A common sight during the horse era. Men and horses take a break. Harness removed.

Light cart harness

Trap harness and rope reins for a good all-rounder.

Right: *Jim Reynolds sets a ridge or rigg, using open bridles. Horsemen have debated open v closed bridles since harness was invented. Closed bridles have winkers or blinkers.*

Basic plough harness, with no frills.

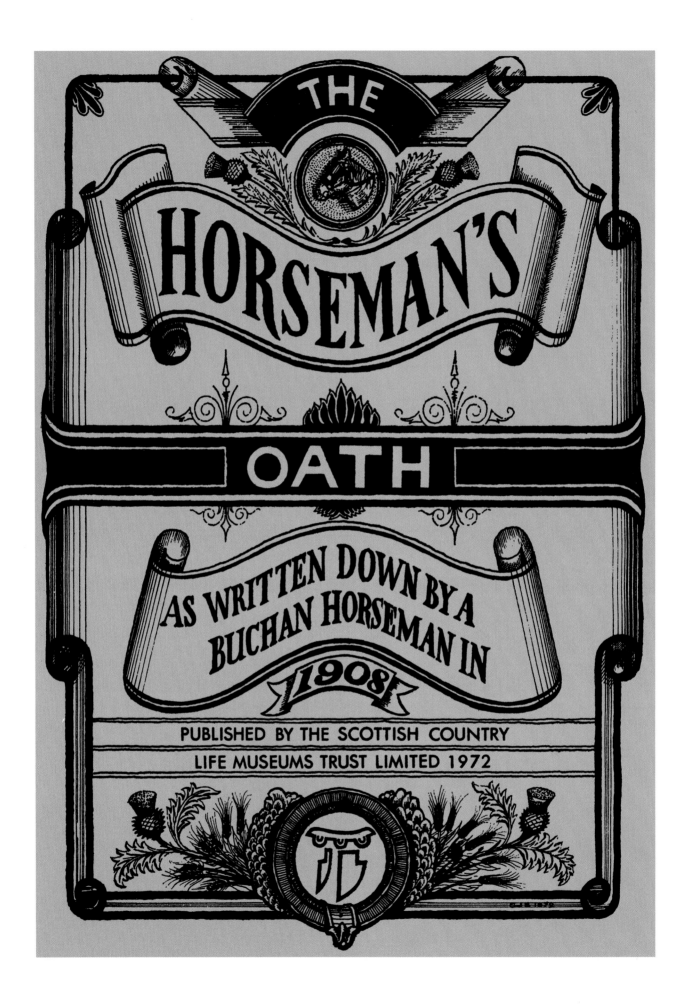

THE HORSEMAN'S OATH

AS WRITTEN DOWN BY A BUCHAN HORSEMAN IN 1908

PUBLISHED BY THE SCOTTISH COUNTRY LIFE MUSEUMS TRUST LIMITED 1972

The Oath

I of my own free will and accord solemnly vow and swear before God and all these witnesses that I will heal, conceal, and never reveal any part of the true horsemanship which I am about to receive at this time. Furthermore I solemnly vow and swear that I will neither write it nor indite, cut it nor carve it on wood or stone, nor yet on anything moveable or immoveable under the canopy of heaven, nor yet so much as wave a finger in the air to none but a horseman.

Furthermore I vow and swear that I will never give it nor see it given to a tradesman of any kind except to a blacksmith or a veterinary surgeon or a horse-soldier. Furthermore I will never give it nor see it given to a farmer or a farmers son unless he be working his own or his fathers horses. Furthermore I will never give it nor see it given to a fool nor a madman nor to my father nor mother sister nor brother nor to any womankind. Furthermore I will never give it nor see it given to my wife nor daughter nor yet to the very dearest ever lay by my side. Furthermore I will never give it nor see it given to anyone after sunset on Saturday night nor before sunrise on Monday morning. Furthermore, I will neither abuse nor bad use any man's horses with it and if I see a brother do so I will tell him of his fault. Furthermore I will never advise anyone to get it nor disadvise anyone from getting it but leave every one to his own free will and accord. Furthermore I will never give it nor see it given to any under the age of sixteen nor above the age of forty-five. Furthermore I will never give it nor see it given unless there be three or more lawful sworn brethren present after finding them to be so by trying and examining them. Furthermore I will never give it nor see it given for less than the sum of £1 sterling or the value thereof. Furthermore I will never refuse to attend a meeting if warned within three days except in a case of riding fire or going for the doctor, and if I fail to keep these promises may my flesh be torn to pieces with a wild horse and my heart cut through with a horseman's knife and my bones buried on the sands of the seashore where the tide ebbs and flows every twenty-four hours so that there may be no remembrance of me amongst lawful brethren so help me God to keep these promises. Amen.

Previous Spread:
The Horseman's Word.

Left: *Taut chains to the swingletree means that this team is really pulling.*

Working trace harness, with typical cart bridles. The single horse on the left of lighter build was probably for 'running about' jobs.

Left: This painting from Antwerp Museum shows not only the colourful harness but also the brutality to which willing horses were only too often subject.

Nineteenth century winter scene of a timber drag.

This attractive card was sent to J. Beasley, blacksmith at Woodend, Hockley Heath, Birmingham.

A study in patch work. A huddle of strong coloured horses for sale.

Heavy horse shoes in competition at the Royal Highland Show, Ingliston, Edinburgh.

Billy Cammidge in his blacksmith's shop at Flower Hill Farm, North Newbould, East Riding, then a thriving visitor centre.

Mervyn Ramage's roan Clydesdale shows complete lack of concern about whatever happens at the Great Yorkshire Show.

For what we are about to receive. . .

Housens fitted above the hames were originally to prevent rain seeping between neck and collar. They are a south of England feature, now mainly decorative.

Artillery harness is of necessity as simple as possible.

Workmanlike but decorative. Suffolk pair at a ploughing match.

*A pile of wood blocks from wr
wheel hubs or naves will be se
ed and shaped. Examined by
author, whose grandfather wc
joiner and wheelwright.*

Scene at a farm implements sale. The author recollects the feel of the horse hoe.

This late 1990s dispersal sale in the East Riding attracted the crowds. Sissons of Beswick, the owners, were former Wolds waggon makers.

Moving at a smart trot. The white terrier is in typical pose.

A skewbald and a light rulley are much more entertaining than a van.

The wide hand rake shown here was for clean raking after the crop had been piked or led.

Coloured horses of this stamp are strong enough for a plough team.

Left: *The traditional skill of hooping a wheel. The iron tyre is put on hot, and quickly and systematically cooled with water to make it shrink onto the wooden wheel. At work: Wilf Collingwood, Tom Howell and John Harris.*

Station cart made by Marwyn Messer, based on information from books. As no lathe was available, the wheels were made in artillery design.

Marwyn and Rosemary Messer's 15-months-old gelding being long-reined, an indispensable part of training.

Brasses

Fig. 44.—Cross

In line for the Best Decorated Pair, or Cleanest Harness, showing the brasses to good effect.

HORSE BRASSES

At one time horse brasses were the main, and sometimes the only, mans of beautifying a heavy horse. Horse brass collection is now so widespread that it has become a separate branch, witnes the special sales of brasses by Thimbleby and Shoreland, Reading. Formerly they were included in the heavy horse and carriage sales.

Terry Keegan, The Oxleys, Clows Top, Kidderminster, Worcestershire, is the main supplier of harness decorations to the heavy horse world. He states that the main show ring requirements are brasses of good quality; their age matters less. A few exhibitors have a collection of superb antique brasses which they use, but in general these would not have much advantage over bright modern ones. Judges may not know whether the brasses are old or new. Old ones can be faked, and their detection is beyond the scope of the average turnout judge.

Brasses figure little in turnout classes in most areas. There wil be a face piece, and perhaps a breastplate or martingale sporting four or more brasses, but generally few others.

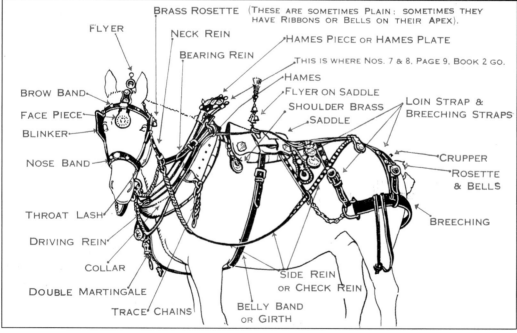

This page and opposite: *From HS Richards' Horse Brass Collections 1944*

Horsemen in the Midlands and south and south-west England favour bells and terrets. 'It grieves me that the only bells obtainable do not have a nice ring', said Terry Keegan. 'For a good tone a bell must be turned rather than cast, but the cost of that operation simply prices itself out of the market.'

Ear muffs are in demand in the Midlands and south-east, but seldom elsewhere. Their original function was to guard against flies. They are obtainable in bright colours, to very smart effect.

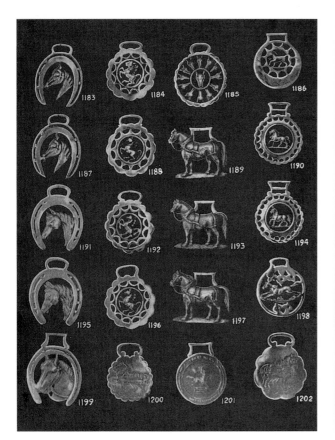

Crescents and stars were always favourites among horsemen.

The Churchill Brass, 1944.

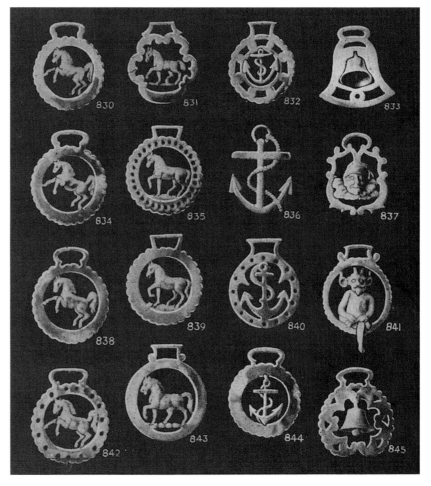

Eight good horse types in the two left hand columns.

Below: *A wonderful display of brasses taken from working animals. Site is the Suffolk Horse Museum, Woodbridge, Suffolk.*

A kidney strap adds to the sense of occasion.

147

Welcoming sign at Ted Dunning's Shire stud, Whixley, York.

Right: Continental style with lots of bells.

The housens topping the collars are a particular feature of this nice pair of greys. Housens were originally designed to keep rain from running down underneath the collars, and are more a southcountry feature.

Everything is neat about this pair. Bridles are clean, winkers blacked, even the yellow coupling bands are eye-catching, while the reins or strings are sparkling white.

Terrets are a feature of this plough harness. If it doesn't win a prize there must be some good ones.

A Decorated Harness class at a country show is one of summer's pleasantest aspects.

Decorated farm implement seats. There are now some wonderful collections.

Best Decorated line-up after a Herefordshire ploughing match.

CONCLUSION

I hope the reader has enjoyed this trip through time. It has been a pleasure to write, chiefly through the contacts with those farmers and farm workers who used the machines described, and the growing number of enthusiasts who seek out and renovate the old machines and vehicles. Modern materials and designs are being used to pass on the torch. As this book shows, horse drawn implements have always been evolving, though change was slowed down when a period of agricultural depression occurred, as between the two World Wars. Survival rather than innovation became, of necessity, the prime mover.

There is now a growing movement to do things with horses as well as show them. We are indeed fortunate that the four heavy breeds, Clydesdale, Percheron, Shire and Suffolk, now augmented by the Ardennes, were preserved in the nick of time in the early 1970s.

In the late 1950s and right through the 1960s, heavy horses seemed on the way out. Few foals were bred. Those that were had difficulty in finding a market. Farmers and others covered a mare or two for old time's sake, rearing, caring for and becoming fond of the resulting foals, only for the butcher to be the only bidder. No wonder so many said: 'Never again'.

Now trained heavies are back in demand, often to haul some of the carts, wggons and implements shown here. Not only are they a great attraction at shows, but their use in a range of practical jobs strengthens the brotherhood of all concerned .

A spirit of generosity exists among people who work the big horses. They help each other on every conceivable occasion, and if this book helps promote care of the horses and their equipment, vehicles and implements, it will have been well worth while.

A bonny Clydesdale pair. Scottish high peak collars are a load in themselves for a human. North of England peaked collars may be less tall, though still peaked.

A North American eight-horse hitch vividly dressed out.

Further Reading

Anderson, G. M. *From the Glens to the Lowlands,* New Horizon, 1979.

Arnold, James. *The Farm Waggons of England and Wales,* David & Charles, 1979.

— *All Drawn by Horses,* David & Charles, 1979.

Baird, Eric. *The Clydesdale Horse,* Batsford, 1982.

Bowden, Charles. *The Last Horseman:* A Year at Sillywrea, Granada, 2001.

Carr, Samuel. *The Poetry of Horses,* Batsford, 1981.

Chivers, Keith. *The Shire Horse,* J.A. Allen, 1977, and Futura (abridged), 1978.

— *The London Harness Horse Parade:* A Centenary History, J.A. Allen, 1985.

Chivers and Rayner, *The Heavy Horse Manual,* David & Charles, 1981.

Cobbett, William. *Rural Rides,* Penguin Books, 1967.

Cockcroft, Barry. *Princes of the Plough,* Dent, 1977.

Cummings, Primrose. *The Great Horses,* Dent, 1946.

Day, Herbert. *Horses on the Farm,* Hutton Press, 1981.

— *My Life with Horses,* Hutton Press, 1983.

Dent, Anthony. *Donkey,* Harrap, 1972.

— *Cleveland Bay Horses,* J.A. Allen, 1978.

Ernle, Lord. *English Farming Past and Present,* Heinemann, 1968 (sixth edition).

Evans, George Ewart. *The Horses in the Furrow,* Faber & Faber, 1960.

— *Ask the Fellows Who Cut the Hay,* Faber & Faber, 1956.

— *The Farm and the Village,* Faber & Faber, 1969.

— *The Pattern Under the Plough,* Faber & Faber, 1966.

— *Horse Power and Magic,* Faber & Faber, 1979.

Fussell, G.E. *The Old English Farming Books (1523-1793)* Aberdeen Rare Books, 1978.

Gibbs-Smith, Charles H. *The Bayeux Tapestry,* Phaidon, 1973.

Gilbey, Sir Walter Bt. *The Concise History of the Shire Horse,* Spur Publications, 1976. (First published in 1899.)

— *Farmstock of Old,* Spur Publications, 1976. (First published in 1910.)

Gladwin, D. D. *The Waterways of Britain,* Batsford, 1976.

Hadfield, Charles. *British Canals,* David & Charles, 1974.

— *The Canals of South and South East England,* David & Charles, 1969.

Hart, Edward. *Shire Horses,* Batsford, 1983.

— *Care and Showing of the Heavy Horse,* Batsford, 1981.

— *Heavy Horses,* Batsford, 1981.

— *Golden Guinea Book of Heavy Horses, Past and Present,* David & Charles, 1976.

— *Pony Trekking,* David & Charles, 1976.

— *Showing Livestock,* David & Charles, 1979.

— *Victorian and Edwardian Farming from Old Photographs,* Batsford, 1981.

— *The Heavy Horse,* Shire Publications, 1979.

Hayes, Captain M. Horace, FRCVS, *Veterinary Notes for Horse Owners,* Stanley Paul, 1974 (sixteenth edition)

Hennel, Thomas. *The Old Farm,* Robinson Publishing, 1984.

Hogg, Garry. *Hammer and Tongs, Blacksmithery Down the Ages.* Hutchinson, 1964.

Holden, Bryan. *The Long Haul,* J.A. Allen, 1985.

Hughes, G.B. *Horse Brasses for the Collector,* Country Life, 1964.

Ingram, Arthur. *Horse-Drawn Vehicles since 1760,* Blandford, 1977.

Janovich, Miklos. *They Rode into Europe,* Harrap,

Other Titles by Edward Hart

Book of the Heavy Horse

The Coloured Horse and Pony

Care and Showing of the Heavy Horse

The Dry Stone Wall Handbook

The Golden Guinea Book of Heavy Horses, Past and Present

Heavy Horses

Heavy Horses: an Anthology

The Heavy Horse

The Harness Horse (with Audrey Hart)

Hedge Laying and Fencing: the Countryman's Art Explained

The Hill Shepherd

Northcountry Farm Animals

Scottish Farm Animals

Pony Trekking

Shepherds' Crooks and Walking Sticks (with David Grant)

Walking Sticks (with Len Parkin)

Your Sheepdog and its Training (with Tim Longton)

The Sheep Dog: its Work and Training (with Tim Longton)

Sheep: a Guide to Management

Shire Horses

Showing Livestock

Sheepkeeping on a Small Scale

Victorian and Edwardian Farming from Old Photographs

Working Dogs (with Audrey Hart)

The Year Round

Glossary

Apron: garment worn by all drivers of turn-outs.

Arve: instruction to horse, turn left.

Balk: strip of land in a field left unploughed.

Bell crank: lever with two arms, having a common fulcrum at their place of joining.

Bevelled shoe: slopes outwards to make the foot appear bigger.

Binder: reaping machine that both cuts and binds corn in sheaves. Also known as a reaper binder or string binder. Early types used wire but later types used string or twine.

Blaze: white marking down front of face; a lot of white is known as 'bald-headed' in the USA

Blinds, blinders: blinkers.

Blinkers: also known as winkers, Leather eye shades, worn by horses in draught, to prevent them catching a glimpse of the following load.

Bobbins: rounded wooden members used to prevent the chafing of traces against the flanks of a horse.

Box seat: high front seat on certain horse-drawn vehicles and implements. Originally a box containing valuables, on which the driver sat to ensure their safety. Later a tool box.

Brasses: horse brasses worn as a decoration and amulet.

Breast collar: encircles the chest, being more of a band than a collar. Only used for light work.

Breast: curved part of the plough that turns the furrow.

Brecham: Scots word for collar, the peaked or peakit brecham being the Scottish peaked collar, also called the tappit (crested) brecham and the Glasgow pike.

Breechings: are located over the back and hindquarters and attached to the saddle. They perform a complementary function to the collar by enabling a horse to lean backwards into the load, slow it down, stop or reverse it.

Breed class: shown to breed standards, without harness or vehicle (see 'In-hand').

Bridle: system of head and face straps worn by a horse, forming attachments for bit and reins.

Brig: bridge on the saddle.

Broadcast: sow seed or distribute manure in a random manner. Seed was often sown in this way by hand, the sower flinging handfuls alternately left and right as he walked the furrows. Box-type machines and seed fiddles were later introduced.

Browband: leather strap across the face of a horse, forming part of the bridle.

By: designates sire.

Cart gear: harness for a carthorse with pad saddle and breeching, as used in drawing a cart or waggon.

Cart lodge: shed, usually thatched, in a farmyard or the corner of a field, where a cart or implement may be kept. Open-sided but with enough cover to keep off the worst of wind and rain.

Cart: two-wheeled vehicle with shafts.

Cartwright: Cart builder and repairer. (Scotland.)

Castrate: make incapable of breeding (male.)

Chain harness: draught harness for heavy work, based on chains rather than on leather straps.

Chain horse: extra horse working in chains or chain harness, preceding a shaft horse in tandem.

Chains: chain traces used by chain horses.

Clean-legged: free of long hair or feather on lower legs; Percherons and Suffolks are clean-legged breeds.

Clover: forage legume of particular value to horses; can be made into hay.

Clyde: Clydesdale horse. The heavy draught horse of Scotland.

Coachman: driver of a vehicle with two or more horses.

Cob: short stocky equine, between a horse and a pony. Can be ridden or driven.

Cobbletree: wooden or metal bar joining swingletrees to implement in multiple yokes. Also called a baulk, evener or maisletree.

Cogs: studs fitted to horseshoes for icy conditions, also called pikes.

Collar: draught or neck collar worn by a pulling horse, to which other items of harness are attached, allowing it greater purchase for hauling.

Collecting ring: adjacent to the showing ring, where exhibits meet just before entry.

Colt: young male horse, uncastrated.

Combine: combine harvester that replaced the

reaper binder during the twentieth century, although not widely used in Britain until the 1940s. Early types were drawn by about 40 horses per hitch. It cut and threshed in one action.

Come on: instruction to horse, set off.

Coulter tube: combined tube and coulter on a seed drill.

Coulter: vertical cutting knife mounted on the front of a plough. This opened the way for the horizontal slice of the share.

Coup cart: tip cart; coup is the Scots word for tip.

Crown: three or more furrows made by the plough at the start of a ploughing match.

Crownpiece: leather strap worn on top on the bridle, above the poll.

Crupper: loop-strap to retain the tail of a draught horse.

Cultivator: machine used in breaking up the sods of a ploughed field. Form of harrow on wheels, the tines or teeth fixed to bars behind rear travelling wheels. Each tine may be adjusted individually.

Decorated class: class where the harness and its decorations are of more consequence than the horse itself.

Digging stick: primitive hand tool used like a pickaxe or mattock, later replaced by the plough.

Dodie hames: low hames to go with the dodie collar.

Dodie: non-peaked collar, a term used in North-east Scotland.

Doubles: pair of horses, a team.

Drachts: Draught chains.

Drag: heavy harrow, almost a cultivator.

Draught pole: used on certain horse-drawn vehicles and implements. An attachment between draught animals and the load they hauled. Horse were hitched in pairs on either side of a pole.

Draught: the ability of a towing animal to move its load. Hauling a load, and the condition of hauling. Horse kept for hauling rather than riding or pack work are known as 'draught' horses. These may be heavy draught or cart horses and light draught horses for coaches, carriages and smaller vehicles. There are also draught ponies and cobs. Also 'draft' (USA).

Draughts: swingletrees (see below.)

Dray: four-wheeled vehicle with seat, brewers' vehicles are usually termed drays.

Drill: machine invented or perfected by Jethro Tull about 1702. Used for sowing in neat drills or rows as opposed to the wasteful method of broadcasting.

Drills: long neat rows, depressed by the foot of a coulter tube on a drill, used for drilling or machine sowing.

Driver: person in charge of a horse or horses and vehicle.

Drug bat, shoe: types of brake used on cart or waggon.

Dwang: lever for tightening securing chains, say round a load of timber; also called a sylvester.

Dynamometer: device for recording the pull of a horse team, without the team moving a stoneboat.

Elevator: stackyard machine of a portable type used for the mechanical stacking of hay and corn sheaves.

End door: removable wooden fitment, not hinged, at the back of the cart, lifted off to allow tipping.

Entire: stallion.

Face piece: strap hanging from brow band of bridle and carrying a brass decoration. Also called a face brass, facer, for plate, or fore brass.

Feather: long hair on the legs of a horse, especially a Shire horse or Clydesdale.

Feed basket: feed basket made of withies, Worn by a horse while feeding at its work and on the move.

Feed-barrel: barrel or similar container in which corn and bran, etc., may be kept.

Felloes, fellies: wooden section of the circumference of the iron-tyred wheel.

Filly: young female horse, usually used in conjunction with age definition, i.e. filly foal.

Finger bar: slotted bar in which the fingers or cutting blades of a mower slide from side to side in cutting the crop.

Fingers: the flattened, wedge-shaped knife blades of a mowing or reaping machine.

Finish: in ploughing, the place where the furrows meet from opposite directions.

Flags, noppins, sprigs, standards, tossles: decorations standing above the plaited mane, fashioned out of straw, wire or ribbon.

Fly head terret, fly-terret: brass ornament fitted to top of head strap or collar.

Forge: place where a horse may be shod.

Fox-hunting: A method of ploughing where a group follow one another round the field rather than taking individual sections.

Furr: see 'Furrow'.

Furrow horse: off-side horse, the right-hand one from the plough stilts. Some furrow horses are trained to walk just clear of the furrow, but retain the name.

Furrow slice: strip or slice of soil that has been cut and transferred by the plough.

Furrow wheel: large wheel that runs in the bottom of the furrow, adjustable for width and depth.

Furrow: groove or trench made by the plough in the soil.

Gaumers, ladders or racks: wooden framework set almost perpendicular from front and rear of cart or waggon.

Gear: term for the harness of a horse.

Gee back: instruction to horse, turn right.

Gee on: instruction to horse, set off.

Gelding: castrated male.

Girth: measurement around the centre of the back, also the band round the body attached to the saddle.

Glasgow jock: fibre used to make the ties or securing ropes for horse lorry haps or covers.

Glasgow pike: see 'Brecham'.

Groom: in the show world, the assistant in charge of a horse, or the assistant to the coachman, riding with the vehicle.

Grubber: type of cultivator, the tines of which were mainly in advance of the rear wheels. Adjusted by vertical lift of the whole machine.

Hake: notched vertical loop, for draught purposes, at the front of a plough. Attached to the frame by means of a horizontal quadrant.

Half-clip: to clip a horse's coat around its legs and lower belly. Done in winter to stop the coat holding sweat after exertion, which can chill the horse and cause illness.

Halter: bitless headpiece of light hemp, used when catching the horse and tying in stable. Often worn under bridle and then used for tying up.

Hames: wooden or iron bars on a neck collar to which rein rings are attached and also hooks for the trace or shaft chains to be fitted. Joined at the bottom (in pairs) by hooks and at the top by chains or straps. Also known as 'Tees'.

Handles: part of the plough held by the ploughman.

Hands: the width of a man's hand, said to be an average measurement of four inches. Used in measuring the height of a horse from ground level to the withers or top of the shoulders.

Hap: tarpaulin cover for the load on a horse or motor lorry.

Harrow: flat implement with teeth or spikes on the underside. Used in breaking up the clods of ploughland or covering the seedbed after sowing.

Hay lifter: elevator towed behind a hay cart, used in raising hay from the windrows to the loading platform. This cut out much of the heavy manual work with a pitchfork.

Hay sledge: a small flat cart or wheel-less vehicle used in collecting hay on mountains and moorland farms. A larger vehicle with wheels might overturn on steep slopes.

Hay sweep: appliance with long wooden bars, tipped with iron or steel, for gathering up hay from the swathe with a scooping motion.

Headland: the end of the furrows, where the teams turn. It cannot therefore be left in neat furrows and must be gone over when the rest of the field is complete.

Headstall: see Bridle.

Hig: instruction to the horse to turn left (Aberdeen)

High-cut: unbroken furrow set on edge.

Hip: instruction to the horse to move forwards (Aberdeen)

Hitch: the means of securing a horse to its load.

Horse fork: simple pulley-lift with a grab device, for lifting hay from wagon to rick. Operated by a draught house walking backwards and forwards. Replaced by the elevator.

Housen: part of the harness, located behind the upper part of the collar and fastened to the hames.

Hub caps, cups: caps which screw into the wheel centre and are packed with grease.

In-hand: synonymous with 'breed class'; a single animal shown, usually under breed society standards.

Ins and Outs: ploughing term for the places at which the plough penetrates and is withdrawn from the soil at the end of a furrow.

Irish collar: open collar that buckles at the top, also called an Ulster collar.

Janker: see Monkey.

Kidney strap, neck strap: strap from collar to draft chains, solely for carrying decorations.

Knife bar: the same as a finger bar, supporting the blades of a mower or reaper.

Ladders: detachable ladder-like structures at either end of a vehicle to help support an overhanging load.

Land cap: metal bar on the side of a plough to keep it steady and hold back the soil above the furrow.

Land horse: near side horse; the left one from the plough stilts.

Land wheel: small wheel that runs on the unploughed land, adjustable.

Land wheels: the wheels of a farm implement supporting it during work on the land. On a plough the smaller of two front wheels supporting the weight of the machine on the landward side away from the furrow.

Landside: flat part of the wheel that presses against the furrow wall.

Lead rope: Scots word for a halter.

Linen van: van with a canvas cover or tilt.

Mare: female from three years onwards.

Martingale or False martingale: connecting strap worn between the forelegs of a horse, forming attachment for the breastplate.

Meeter, metre, or meter straps: attach collar and hames to cart saddle.

Monkey: four-wheeled pole vehicle with adjustable rear axle for long loads like timber, pipes or ironwork; also called a janker.

Mouldboard: part of a plough that lays or turns back the furrow, directly behind the share. Either all metal or metal-sheathed. Its height and shape decide the form and angle of the furrow. (see 'breast').

Mouth: of horses: to render the horse's mouth tender so as to make it more responsive to the bit, and to accustom it to having a bit in its mouth.

Naff, nave: hub of a wooden wheel.

Nose bowl: wooden container from which a horse feeds while on the move. Similar to a nose can.

Nose can: brightly painted tin can from which a horse feeds while on the move. Similar to a feed basket.

Obstacle test: a race against time by turn-outs through a series of markers.

Open bridle: one without blinkers or blinders, so the horse can see what is behind it. Those favouring the open bridle believe the horse is less nervous when it can see the reason for any noise.

Out of: designates dam.

Pawls: the raised part of gears on machines and implements, working against a small lever or ratchet. These are responsible for the clicking noise of mowers and reapers.

Percheron: a breed of heavy horse originating in France.

Pikes: see 'Cogs'.

Pitching: raising hay or sheaves of corn on to rick or cart by means of pitchforks.

Plough body: see 'breast'.

Plough gear: the trace harness of a plough horse without cart pad or breeching.

Plow: old English spelling of plough, still used in the United States of America.

Point of draft: the point from which a horse pulls to maximum advantage. It is sited just in front of the shoulders and in line with its own centre of gravity and that of the object being pulled. The modern neck collar is designed to enable the horse to pull at its point of draft.

Point, sock, share: detachable metal point that leads the plough body into the ground. It makes the horizontal cut. Plough points became rather a fetish among ploughmen and before 1939 an incredible range was manufactured. These were standardised to three during World War Two and no-one was worse off.

Pole: same as draught pole.

Pulling contest: one or two horses pulling a loaded sledge over a certain distance, the winner continuing to do so when others have failed; the pull may also be recorded on a 'dynamometer'.

Punch: The Suffolk Punch. A heavy draught horse of East Anglia.

Pyke: a small rick or haycock.

Quart: to plough at ninety degrees to existing furrows, a method used in fallowing.

Quarter strap: harness strap worn across the loins.

Reaper: a machine designed for cutting corn rather than grass, but sometimes used for either.

Red ticket: first prize.

Rick lifter: low cart onto which haycocks may be winched for transport. Used mainly in Scotland and the north of England.

Ridge: a section of a field marked out to be ploughed as one piece.

Riding machine: machine or implement with a seat for the driver, usually found on heavier and more modern types of equipment than the old-style walking machine.

Rig: 1. any type of machine or vehicle. Also a collective noun for horses, vehicles and harness. 2. The ridge of a stack.

Rigwiddy: Back chain, the Central Scottish term, but rigwoddy or rigwoodie in North-east Scotland.

Ring: area in which animals are shown.

Rollers: alternative name for bobbins.

Rosette: flat, rounded disc shaped ornament at the junction between browband, throatlash and cheek-straps.

Rulley, rully: four-wheeled flat-topped vehicle, usually with shafts for one horse but no seat.

Saddle: a cart saddle worn by draught horses, consisting of a pad underneath a channel for the chain that takes the weight of the shafts.

Scotch bob: the decorative plaiting of a horse's tail to keep it clean and out of the traces.

Scruffler: a horse harrow designed for use between rows of crops such as turnips.

Seedbed: fine, worked-down soil into which seed is drilled.

Semi-grubber: type of grubber with the bars or tines both in front and behind the main land wheels. Between a grubber and a cultivator.

Shaft horse: also known as a wheeler or thill horse. Works next to the load with a team or tandem pair.

Shank: rope attached to a halter's headpiece.

Share: the pointed and wedge-shaped fitment of a plough, between coulter and mouldboard. This is responsible for the horizontal slice.

Shears: the turntable from which the front wheels of a waggon are suspended to make them steerable.

Shelvings: flat wooden framework around the cart to give greater capacity for bulky loads. Sideboards are removed when shelvings are fitted.

Shim: a hoe, or to cut glancingly with a hoe.

Shire: Shire horse. Typical English heavy draught horse, noted for its combined strength and docility, also for the large amount of feather on its legs.

Shoer: Horseshoer or farrier.

Sideboards: single pieces of wood to add to the capacity of the cart for solid loads. Front board and back board are similarly used

Side-delivery rake: form of rake in which the prongs, in three rows, are mounted diagonally and sideways, throwing out or turning the hay with a sideways movement.

Sinker: Term for the wooden ball at the end of the halter rope. Also called a block, clog, helter cob, manger ball, manger log, nagger, nog, plug, or toggle.

Slade: plough accessory or fitment running in the sole or bottom of the furrow, to balance the plough.

Sledge, stoneboat: wheelless transport used in pulling matches, of a known weight and loaded with blocks whose weights are also known.

Spreader: wooden bar used to space the trace chains apart and prevent rubbing horses' flanks. Also called spread bat, stretch stick, stent, stretcher, or theat bar.

Stalk: extension often used with a bracket to support a small land wheel on a farm implement.

Stallion: male horse capable of breeding.

Steersman: driver in control of a farm machine or of its steering device. Not always in charge of the horses.

Steward: judge's assistant, there to carry out his wishes and facilitate his task.

Stilts: the handles and handgrips of a horse plough.

Stook: several sheaves of corn stacked together, round central air space, for drying.

Strap harness: harness for a light draught horse, made up of leather straps rather than chains.

Stretcher: light wooden pole to keep apart two trace chains when a second horse is hitched to a cart.

String horse: that horse in a team wearing the reins and therefore under the direct control of the driver.

Strings: reins of light rope, coiled and hung on the hames when not in use.

Stripper: combine harvester stripping off the ears of wheat but ignoring the standing straw. Widely used in Australia and North America.

Swath turner: machine with sideways revolving tines used in turning the hay. Less complex than the side-delivery rake.

Swing plough: wooden beamed plough without wheels.

Swing: to accustom a horse to be led while wearing a bridle.

Swingle tree: piece of wood or metal with hooks, joining trace chains and implement and holding the chains apart so that they do not chafe the horses' legs. See 'whippletree'.

Tampcock: small haycock or stack.

Tandem: two draught horses working one behind the other.

Tappit brecham: see 'Brecham'.

Tassels: worn by horses to keep dust and flies out of their eyes.

Tedder: originally a tidder or tidding machine. Box-like machine with revolving tines, used for turning the hay in a backwards direction.

Tees: see 'Hames'.

Temperament: natural disposition, e.g. fiery or placid.

Terrets: rings to guide reins and traces on harness.

Theats: draught chains; a Glasgow term.

Thong: supple plaited cord forming connection between whip-lash and stock or handle.

Threshing box: name usually given to a box-like portable threshing machine. Little used since the coming of the combine and stripper.

Throatlash: diagonal strap of a bridle fitting under the jaw, near the junction of head and neck.

Thrums: knotted bows ornamenting a whip thong. Causes an extra loud crack.

Tilt: canvas cover of a van; see Linen van.

Tines: straight or curved bars or teeth used with a variety of implements. Similar to the prongs of a fork.

Top latch: strap that secures the top of the hames together.

Traces: straps, chains or cords connecting the harness of a horse with its load.

Trackage: marks or furrows left by the land wheels of a heavy machine.

Trade turn-out: normally applied to horses and vehicles used for deliveries or city work, not farm vehicles.

Trams: shafts.

Troch: water trough.

Turn-out: vehicle plus horse(s) in a show class; this is usually for single horse, pair, then three or four or more.

Turnwrest: plough widely used on downland farms in the south of England. The direction of furrow slice could be changed at the end of each row to effect up and down rather than continuous ploughing. This was done by making adjustments on the plough rather than by turning the implement.

Ulster collar: see Irish collar.

Ventholes: holes in a certain type of leather muzzle, allowing a horse wearing the muzzle to breathe.

Waggon: four-wheeled farm vehicle whose style varies according to county of origin.

Wagon: American version of above, also used to denote a motor vehicle.

Walking machine: a machine controlled by a driver or steersman plodding on foot at the side or rear. Not a riding machine.

Wattery chain: the chain of a curb bit, which goes under the chin.

Welsh Cob: light draught horse of Welsh origins, also a dual purpose horse of great courage and strength.

Wheelwright: Cart builder and repairer. (England.)

Whippletree: horizontal bar or bow shape to which the traces of a draught horse may be attached for certain types of gear. Mainly used with a draught pole.

Windrow: drying hay in long neat rows from which it might be either collected directly or made into haycocks.

Winkers: see 'Blinkers'.

Wish: an instruction to the horse to turn right. (Aberdeen.)

Yoking: attaching a horse to conveyance or implement.

Acknowledgements

For unstinting help with information, photographs and production, I would like to thank

Audrey Hart

Beamish Museum

Cheryl Midgley

Clarissa Dickson Wright for her excellent Foreword

Claudia Steele

Diana Zeuner, Heavy Horse World

Gavin Sprott

Geoff Morton

Jane Parkin

Jim Lawson

Joe Godderidge

John Gall

Malcolm Coward

Norman Jones

Roger Clark

Rosemary Cooper

Roy Fox

Sally Mitchell

Sophie Hill

Terry Keegan, for encouragement and use of his
large collection of heavy horse material.